CLUES

1

Across

1 Large number (9)
6 Vehicle (3)
8 Light cake (6)
9 Notions (5)
10 Domesticated polecat (6)
11 Country (7)
13 Slow and steady (7)
16 Naval flag (6)
18 Leisurely walk (5)
19 Travelling case (6)
21 Mr Lynam, TV presenter (3)
22 Impediment (9)

Down

1 Cleaning item (3)
2 Of the moon (5)
3 Inactivity (7)
4 Ill-advised or foolish (6)
5 Skin condition (6)
7 Abode or home (9)
8 Defend or protect (9)
12 Meat-axe (7)
14 Waylay (6)
15 Irregular (6)
17 Hairdresser's establishment (5)
20 Diocese (3)

Across

1 Surgeon's knife (7)
5 Movie (4)
7 Snooker rod (3)
8 Determined (8)
9 Wanders (5)
10 Wet weather (4)
13 Prod (4)
14 Neat (4)
18 Nobleman (4)
19 Expend (3,2)
21 Wading bird (8)
22 Anger (3)
23 Water jug (4)
24 Aims (7)

Down

1 Safety (8)
2 Australian city (8)
3 Die (6)
4 Reflected light (6)
5 Stimulus or incentive (6)
6 Plenty (4)
11 Aircraft's sudden plunge (4,4)
12 Defenceless (8)
15 Complain whiningly (6)
16 Celestial body (6)
17 Quality of being funny (6)
20 Decelerate (4)

3

Across

1 Small restaurant (6)
4 Go in (5)
7 Urgent or commanding (10)
8 Prayer ending (4)
9 Permitted by law (5)
11 Temporal (7)
13 Act (7)
15 Heaps (5)
17 Permits (4)
18 Funeral director (10)
20 Heathen (5)
21 Ballerina (6)

Down

1 Baas (6)
2 At that time (4)
3 Cover and extend beyond (7)
4 Evict (5)
5 In addition (3)
6 Regal (5)
7 Drawing implement (6)
10 Glare (6)
12 Referee's item (3,4)
14 Boy's title (6)
15 Rotund (5)
16 Warning device (5)
17 Lacking fat (4)
19 Use a spade (3)

4

Across

1 Subjugated (11)
7 Single entity (4)
8 Withstand (7)
9 Belonging to him (3)
10 Small twig (5)
11 Crossbreed (6)
13 Cured or smoked ham (6)
16 Merriment (5)
18 Mr Danson, actor (3)
19 Result (7)
20 Sea eagle (4)
21 Malaysian city (5,6)

Down

1 Pack animal (6)
2 Wilt (6)
3 Flung (6)
4 Expels (5)
5 Drawing (7)
6 Nine-sided figure (7)
11 Sailor's bed (7)
12 Clerical cap (7)
13 Fancy cake (6)
14 Invented (4-2)
15 First batsman (6)
17 Noisy commotion (3-2)

5

Across

1 Loot (7)
7 Religious festival (6)
8 Draw back (7)
9 Gaelic (4)
10 Close with a bang (4)
12 Put into print (7)
14 Reprimand at length (7)
16 Pronounce indistinctly (4)
18 Couple (4)
20 Function (7)
21 Comment (6)
22 Having died out (7)

Down

1 Sunshade (7)
2 An extremist (5)
3 Far down (4)
4 Entourage (7)
5 In addition to (2,4,2)
6 Population count (6)
11 Of a mother (8)
12 Incite or stimulate (7)
13 Reap (7)
15 Tooth covering (6)
17 Discover knowledge (5)
19 Undiluted (4)

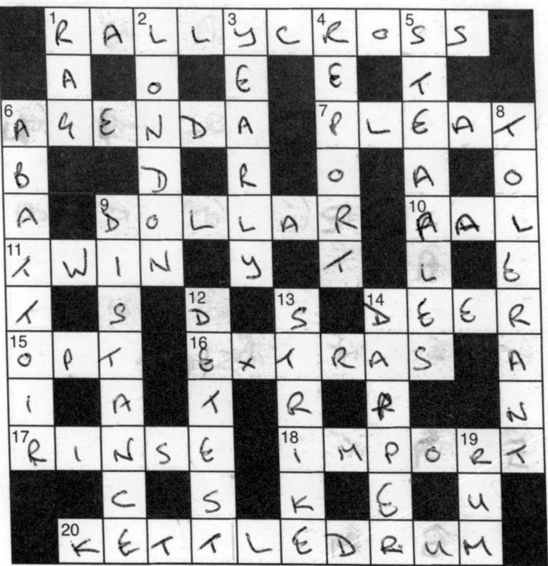

Across

1 Form of motor sport (10)
6 Schedule (6)
7 Fold in clothing (5)
9 Monetary unit (6)
10 Close friend (3)
11 Counterpart (4)
14 Ruminant mammal (4)
15 Choose (3)
16 Crowd actors (6)
17 Wash out (5)
18 Bring in from abroad (6)
20 Percussion instrument (10)

Down

1 Torn cloth (3)
2 English capital (6)
3 Annual (6)
4 Account (6)
5 Spires (8)
6 Slaughterhouse (8)
8 Permissive (8)
9 Remoteness (8)
12 Hate (6)
13 Industrial protest (6)
14 Natty (6)
19 Spirit (3)

7

Across

1 Kitchen item (6,3)
6 Ventilate (3)
8 Outcome (6)
9 Cricket stick (5)
10 Solitary (6)
11 Bacon slices (7)
13 Christening (7)
16 Presuppose (6)
18 Irritates (5)
19 Exalts (6)
21 Nevertheless (3)
22 Artificial language (9)

Down

1 Enemy (3)
2 Youthful (5)
3 Chatters (7)
4 Goes by (6)
5 Temperament (6)
7 Take back (9)
8 Soft fruit (9)
12 Non-professional (7)
14 Courteous (6)
15 Foot part (6)
17 Glossy fabric (5)
20 Zodiac sign (3)

8

Across

1 Elaborate parade (7)
5 Grime (4)
7 Slippery fish (3)
8 Set in motion (8)
9 Raise (5)
10 Overwhelming defeat (4)
13 Fork prong (4)
14 Throw dice (4)
18 Facility (4)
19 Improve (5)
21 Worthy of praise (8)
22 Lyric poem (3)
23 Celebrity (4)
24 Sincere (7)

Down

1 Circular graph (3,5)
2 Easily taken in (8)
3 Expects (6)
4 Teachers (6)
5 Deeply religious (6)
6 Decomposes (4)
11 Tedious (8)
12 Tie for first place (4,4)
15 Stocking run (6)
16 Frail (6)
17 Move swiftly along (6)
20 Desire (4)

9

Across

1 Fabric (6)
4 Perfect (5)
7 Execution by hanging (3,7)
8 Based on fact (4)
9 Short saying (5)
11 Revival or renaissance (7)
13 School bag (7)
15 Stealing (5)
17 Magician's stick (4)
18 Oliver Letwin, say (10)
20 Wooden peg (5)
21 Sport (6)

Down

1 Winner (6)
2 Line in darts (4)
3 Rues (7)
4 Major religion (5)
5 The self (3)
6 Round-up rope (5)
7 Fall awkwardly (6)
10 Iran's capital (6)
12 French bean (7)
14 Women (6)
15 Lukewarm (5)
16 Sum (5)
17 Caution (4)
19 Moo (3)

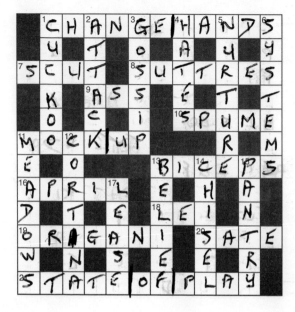

10

Across

1 Pass to another owner (6,5)
7 Rabbit's tail (4)
8 Stitches (7)
9 Donkey (3)
10 Froth (5)
11 Experimental model (4-2)
13 Arm muscle (6)
16 Month (5)
18 Hawaiian garland (3)
19 Paper-folding art (7)
20 Satisfy fully (4)
21 Current situation (5,2,4)

Down

1 Bird (6)
2 Set upon (6)
3 Tittle-tattle (6)
4 Detests (5)
5 Nourish (7)
6 Methods (7)
11 Leas (7)
12 Mediterranean island (7)
13 Credit (6)
14 Hand tool (6)
15 Larder (6)
17 Rental contract (5)

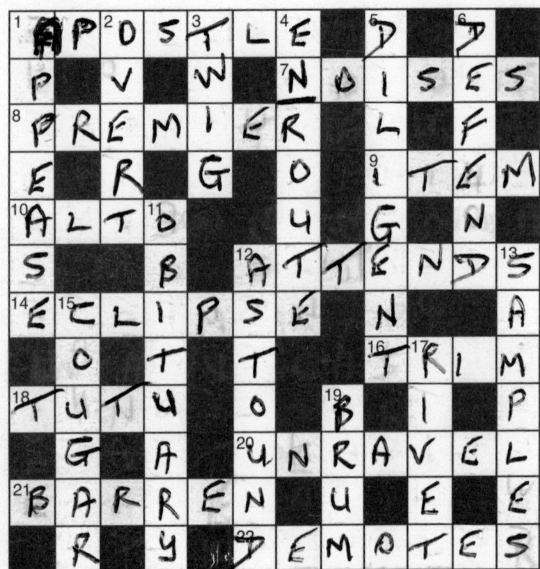

11

Across

1 Disciple (7)
7 Sounds (6)
8 Prime minister (7)
9 Article (4)
10 Male voice (4)
12 Is present at (7)
14 Surpass (7)
16 Prune or clip (4)
18 Ballet skirt (4)
20 Disentangle (7)
21 Sterile (6)
22 Relegates (7)

Down

1 Pacify (7)
2 Open to view (5)
3 Small branch (4)
4 On the way (2,5)
5 Industrious (8)
6 Protect (6)
11 Death notice (8)
12 Bewilder (7)
13 Specimens (7)
15 Puma (6)
17 Fastening pin (5)
19 Birmingham, informally (4)

Across

1 Ratio (10)
6 Stationary (6)
7 Stinging insects (5)
9 Supporting column (6)
10 Whiskey grain (3)
11 Hit at flies (4)
14 Nuisance (4)
15 Snake (3)
16 Counting frame (6)
17 Be alive (5)
18 Thin candles (6)
20 In direct competition (4-2-4)

Down

1 Favourite (3)
2 Set of clothes (6)
3 Supernatural (6)
4 Frustrate (6)
5 Watches carefully (8)
6 Down-to-earth (8)
8 Takes refuge (8)
9 Heaven (8)
12 Squandered (6)
13 Skin decoration (6)
14 Colour (6)
19 Stick or shaft (3)

13

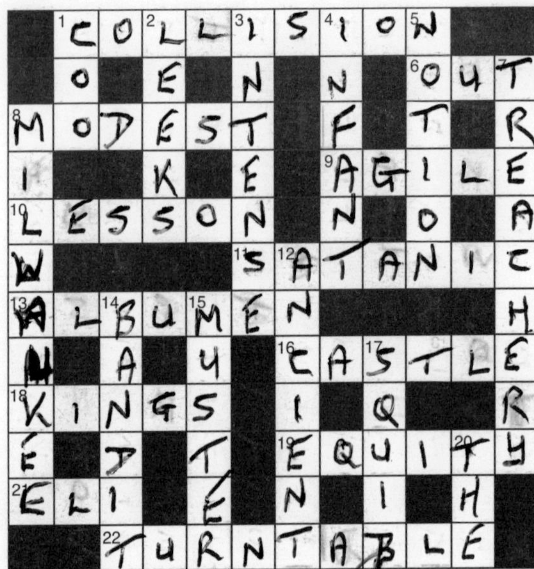

Across

1 Impact (9)
6 On strike (3)
8 Humble (6)
9 Nimble (5)
10 Period of instruction (6)
11 Diabolic (7)
13 Egg white (7)
16 Rook (6)
18 Male monarchs (5)
19 Fairness (6)
21 __ Wallach, actor (3)
22 Revolving platform (9)

Down

1 Dove's cry (3)
2 Vegetables (5)
3 Concentrated (7)
4 Very young child (6)
5 Idea (6)
7 Act of betrayal (9)
8 American city (9)
12 Very old (7)
14 Brigand (6)
15 Summon or gather (6)
17 Firework (5)
20 Definite article (3)

Across

1 Luggage (7)
5 Unspecified amount (4)
7 Boy's name (3)
8 On the quiet (8)
9 Rupture (5)
10 Thoroughfare (4)
13 Cried (4)
14 Observe (4)
18 Simple (4)
19 Liquid (5)
21 Frozen missile (8)
22 Regret (3)
23 Eagerly expectant (4)
24 Crime against the state (7)

Down

1 Australian city (8)
2 Produce (8)
3 Valuable things (6)
4 Additional performance (6)
5 Teeter (6)
6 Unit of distance (4)
11 False teeth (8)
12 Fish (8)
15 Eavesdrop, informally (6)
16 Despot (6)
17 Dozen (6)
20 Cosy (4)

15

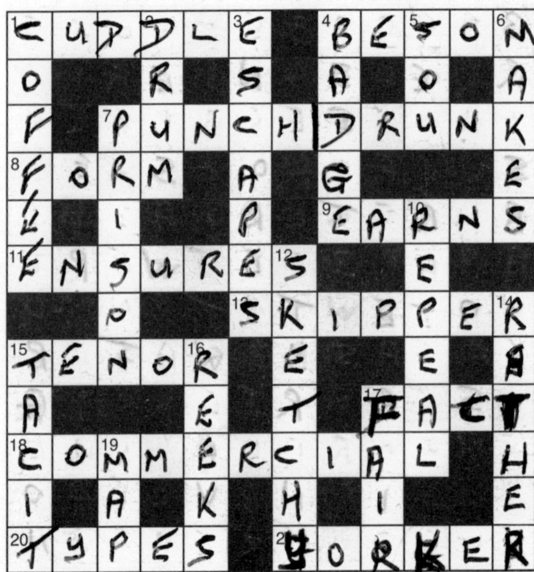

Across

1 Hug (6)
4 Broom of twigs (5)
7 Dazed or stupefied (5-5)
8 Class (4)
9 Deserves (5)
11 Guarantees (7)
13 Sea captain (7)
15 Male voice (5)
17 Datum (4)
18 Mercantile (10)
20 Sorts (5)
21 Cricket delivery (6)

Down

1 Hot beverage (6)
2 Percussion instrument (4)
3 Gets away (7)
4 Emblem (5)
5 Former French coin (3)
6 Manufactures (5)
7 Jail (6)
10 Revoke (6)
12 Superficial or slight (7)
14 Somewhat (6)
15 Unspoken (5)
16 Stinks (5)
17 Impartial (4)
19 Orienteering item (3)

Across

1 Mal de mer (11)
7 Coagulate (4)
8 Fin (7)
9 __ Gardner, actress (3)
10 Happening (5)
11 Powerful or strong (6)
13 Cooks in an oven (6)
16 Traffic markers (5)
18 Perform (3)
19 Spray can (7)
20 Conceal (4)
21 School crossing patrol (8,3)

Down

1 Persian greyhound (6)
2 Add on (6)
3 Notoriety (6)
4 Cutlery item (5)
5 Utter (7)
6 Elfin creatures (7)
11 Mr Howard, MP (7)
12 Army officer (7)
13 Market or exchange (6)
14 National song (6)
15 Sinew (6)
17 Japanese dish (5)

17

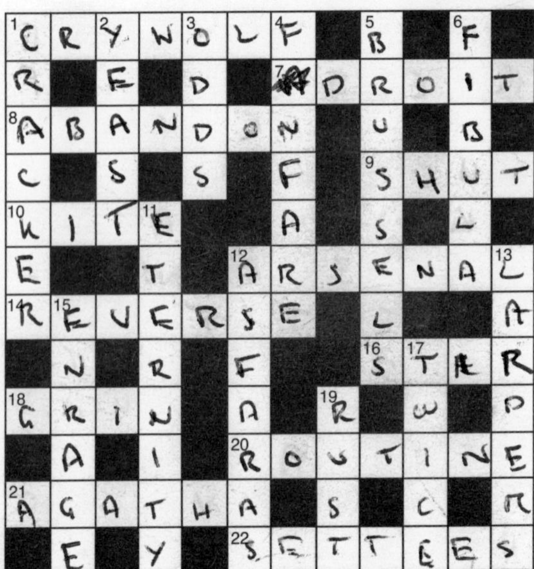

Across

1 Give a false alarm (3,4)
7 Skilful or dexterous (6)
8 Forsake (7)
9 Closed (4)
10 Bird of prey (4)
12 Arms depot (7)
14 Setback (7)
16 Move (4)
18 Broad smile (4)
20 Day-to-day (7)
21 ___ Christie, author (6)
22 Couches (7)

Down

1 Thin crisp biscuit (7)
2 Raising agent (5)
3 Betting chances (4)
4 Flourish of trumpets (7)
5 Belgian capital (8)
6 Leg bone (6)
11 Perpetuity (8)
12 To the extent that (2,3,2)
13 Pantries (7)
15 Provoke to fury (6)
17 Two times (5)
19 Corrode (4)

Across

1 Stadium illumination (10)
6 Freshwater mammals (6)
7 Splendour (5)
9 Spanish dance (6)
10 Egg cells (3)
11 Mountain lake (4)
14 Greek letter (4)
15 Epoch (3)
16 Frightened (6)
17 Molar, say (5)
18 Desire to drink (6)
20 Allure (10)

Down

1 Seizure (3)
2 American state (6)
3 Cleaning cloth (6)
4 Fridge compartment (6)
5 Set apart as sacred (8)
6 Salve (8)
8 Excessively (2,1,5)
9 Escape from prison (5,3)
12 Suds (6)
13 Reviewer (6)
14 Swimming costume (6)
19 Transgression (3)

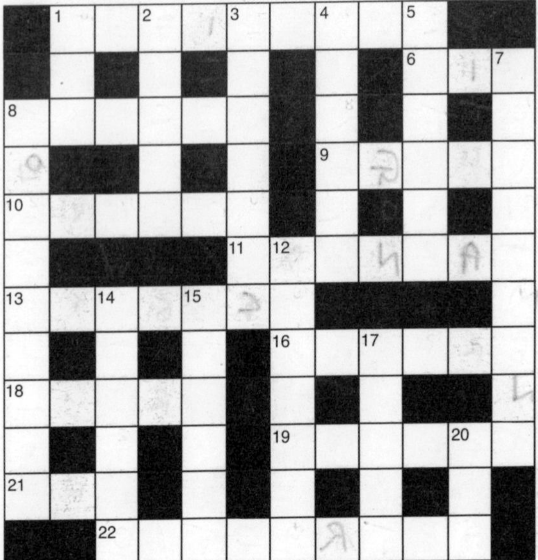

19

Across

1 Warlike (9)
6 Slope downwards (3)
8 Suture, informally (6)
9 Fossil resin (5)
10 Fitting (6)
11 Shipping hazard (7)
13 Raise (7)
16 Country (6)
18 Computer memory units (5)
19 Once more (6)
21 Fish eggs (3)
22 From childhood (3,3,3)

Down

1 Flying mammal (3)
2 Slacken or diminish (3,2)
3 Receive by succession (7)
4 Recently (2,4)
5 Esculent (6)
7 Block of text (9)
8 Month (9)
12 Sure (7)
14 High regard (6)
15 Appoint (6)
17 Rub hard (5)
20 Crafty (3)

Across

1 Portion of food or drink (7)
5 Hairless (4)
7 Curved edge (3)
8 Knock down (8)
9 Cost (5)
10 Midday (4)
13 Unguis (4)
14 Flat (4)
18 Challenge (4)
19 Large sea (5)
21 Shakes (8)
22 Female sheep (3)
23 Talon (4)
24 Withstands (7)

Down

1 Shell fragments (8)
2 Stayed (8)
3 Certainly (6)
4 Zodiac sign (6)
5 English town (6)
6 Speech defect (4)
11 Anonymous (8)
12 Mistakes (8)
15 Lacking width (6)
16 More suitable (6)
17 Brags (6)
20 Watch face (4)

21

Across

1 Sausage, slang (6)
4 Cuban dance (5)
7 Wonderful (10)
8 Heavy metal (4)
9 Hut (5)
11 Extract (4,3)
13 Irregular (7)
15 Additional (5)
17 Amphibian (4)
18 Remorse (10)
20 Ancient language (5)
21 Scamp (6)

Down

1 Coarse fabric (6)
2 Happy and pleased (4)
3 Income (7)
4 Ancient artefact (5)
5 Low (3)
6 Illegal burning (5)
7 Tool type (6)
10 Fastener on a garment (6)
12 Farm vehicle (7)
14 Blunt weapon (6)
15 Surpass (5)
16 Pinny (5)
17 Toddlers (4)
19 Mesh (3)

Across

1 Tightrope walker (11)
7 Mosque prayer leader (4)
8 Most excellent (7)
9 Generation (3)
10 Respond (5)
11 Stops (6)
13 Skirt expander (6)
16 Friends (5)
18 Jam container (3)
19 Herb (7)
20 Paradise (4)
21 Lacking common sense (5-6)

Down

1 Severe food shortage (6)
2 Wanderers (6)
3 Skinflints (6)
4 Shoe part (5)
5 Imprecise (7)
6 Playhouse (7)
11 Write music (7)
12 Belgian province (7)
13 Exclamation of surprise (2,4)
14 Canny (6)
15 Myth (6)
17 Frightening (5)

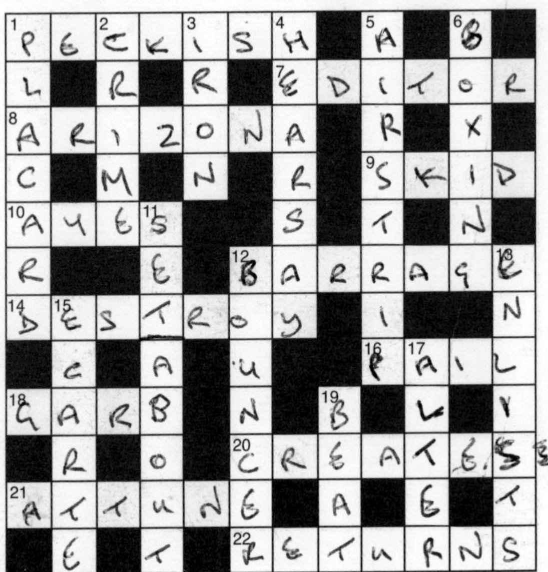

23

Across

1 Slightly hungry (7)
7 Newspaper boss (6)
8 American state (7)
9 Slide sideways (4)
10 Yes votes (4)
12 Heavy artillery fire (7)
14 Ruin (7)
16 Bucket (4)
18 Style of dress (4)
20 Invents (7)
21 Adjust or accustom (6)
22 Goes back (7)

Down

1 Poster (7)
2 Illegal act (5)
3 Golf club (4)
4 Gossip (7)
5 Runway (8)
6 Pugilism (6)
11 Start or begin (3,5)
12 Cricket delivery (7)
13 Joins up (7)
15 Card game (6)
17 Change (5)
19 Defeat (4)

Across

1 Unconquerable (10)
6 State of uproar (6)
7 Direction (5)
9 Piece of small shot (6)
10 Male offspring (3)
11 Horizontal (4)
14 Embraces (4)
15 Congeal (3)
16 Favour (6)
17 Nervy (5)
18 Dapple (6)
20 Again and again (10)

Down

1 Frozen water (3)
2 Fabric (6)
3 That is to say (6)
4 Catch fire (6)
5 Delphinium (8)
6 Tea party, slang (3,5)
8 Good-looking (8)
9 Idiom (8)
12 Globe (6)
13 Allow (6)
14 Made hot (6)
19 Produce eggs (3)

Across

1 Carry on (9)
6 Pinch (3)
8 At the rear of (6)
9 Nutmeg, say (5)
10 Make beloved (6)
11 Senior nurses (7)
13 Foes (7)
16 Choice (6)
18 Long tubes (5)
19 Adjusts (6)
21 Manage (3)
22 Frantic (9)

Down

1 Baked food (3)
2 Uplift (5)
3 Sanction (7)
4 Rubs out (6)
5 Railway locomotive (6)
7 Game birds (9)
8 Apiarist (9)
12 Place apart (7)
14 Disburse (6)
15 Gives out (6)
17 Jewelled headdress (5)
20 Foot digit (3)

Across

1 Proof of purchase (7)
5 Condiment (4)
7 Circuit (3)
8 Tranquil (8)
9 Lustre (5)
10 Young male horse (4)
13 Japanese wrestling (4)
14 Word or expression (4)
18 Stun (4)
19 Wash out (5)
21 Commonplace (8)
22 Mineral (3)
23 This place (4)
24 Indicates or designates (7)

Down

1 Demote (8)
2 Storage unit (8)
3 Mischievous (6)
4 Roofing material (6)
5 Odours (6)
6 Noisy (4)
11 Renegade (8)
12 Having nowhere to live (8)
15 Spite (6)
16 Request forcibly (6)
17 Colouring stick (6)
20 Strong impulse (4)

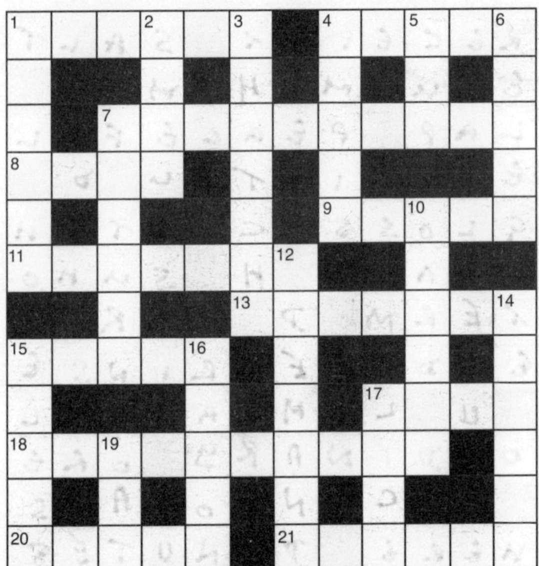

27

Across

1 African desert (6)
4 Mr Costner, actor (5)
7 Fastening for clothes (4,3,3)
8 Inert gas (4)
9 Appears (5)
11 Agreement (7)
13 Extreme or forceful (7)
15 Capture (5)
17 Grain husks (4)
18 Enigmatic (10)
20 Ringlets (5)
21 Male goose (6)

Down

1 Picturesque (6)
2 Soon (4)
3 Clumsy (7)
4 Sorts (5)
5 Contend (3)
6 Requirements (5)
7 Large wasp (6)
10 Goes in (6)
12 Diagram (7)
14 Zodiac sign (6)
15 Child's magazine (5)
16 Takes notice of (5)
17 Be on fire (4)
19 Knight's title (3)

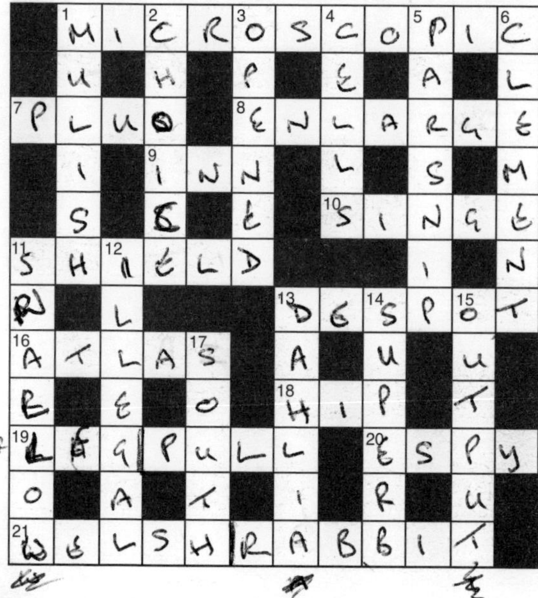

Across

1 Very small (11)
7 As well (4)
8 Make bigger (7)
9 Tavern (3)
10 Scorch (5)
11 Protect (6)
13 Tyrant (6)
16 Book of maps (5)
18 Pelvis (3)
19 Practical joke, informally (3-4)
20 Catch sight of (4)
21 Rarebit (5,6)

Down

1 Stubborn (6)
2 Selection (6)
3 Unlocked (6)
4 Prison rooms (5)
5 Vegetable (7)
6 Merciful (7)
11 Bird (7)
12 Unlawful (7)
13 Perennial plant (6)
14 Excellent (6)
15 Production (6)
17 Compass point (5)

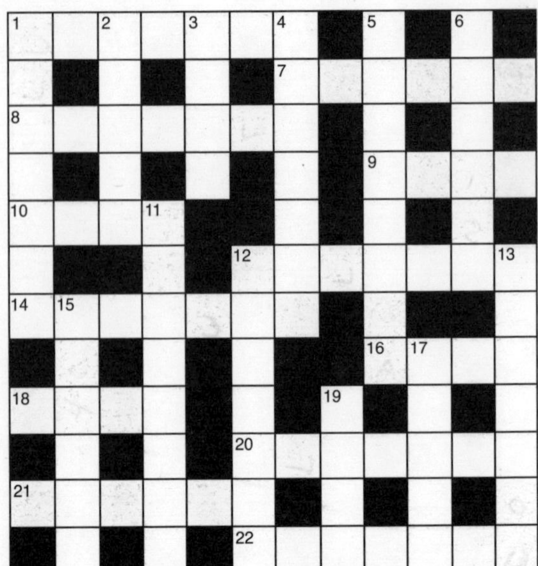

Across

1 Group of four (7)
7 Erase (3,3)
8 Obstinate (7)
9 Musical instrument (4)
10 Impetuous (4)
12 Sleep peacefully (7)
14 Cos, say (7)
16 Shaped mass of bread (4)
18 Footwear item (4)
20 White ant (7)
21 Mild (6)
22 Begrudges (7)

Down

1 Argument (7)
2 Assumed name (5)
3 Skinny (4)
4 Quiver (7)
5 Unnatural (8)
6 Continent (6)
11 Until this time (8)
12 Disperse (7)
13 Roof beams (7)
15 Resounds (6)
17 Edible bulb (5)
19 Makes mistakes (4)

Across

1 Fairground stall (7,3)
6 Recluse (6)
7 Tries out (5)
9 Prairie wolf (6)
10 In addition (3)
11 Mend with stitches (4)
14 Simple card game (4)
15 Meat (3)
16 Shore bird (6)
17 Gasps (5)
18 Mr Spielberg, director (6)
20 Simple (10)

Down

1 Snooker rod (3)
2 Widespread (6)
3 Country (6)
4 Tie up (6)
5 Halting (8)
6 Severe suffering or privation (8)
8 Arachnid (8)
9 Malefactor (8)
12 Kidnapper's demand (6)
13 Toxic substance (6)
14 __ Williams, tennis star (6)
19 Cathedral city (3)

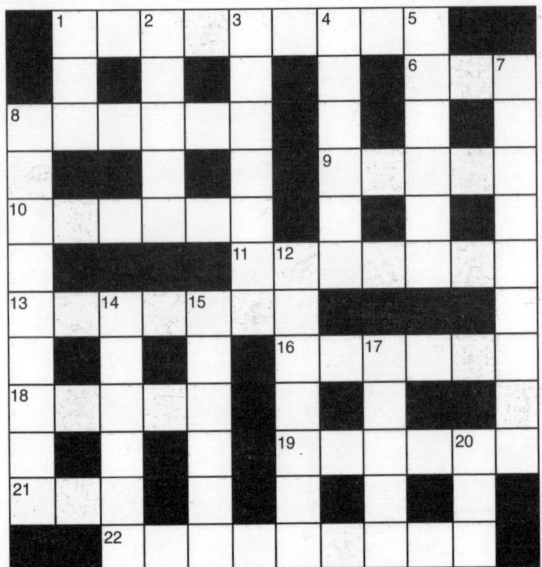

Across

1 Native Australian (9)
6 Edge of a cup (3)
8 Signal fire (6)
9 Auctioneer's hammer (5)
10 Great fear (6)
11 Fundamental nature (7)
13 Cost (7)
16 Neckwear item (6)
18 Foremost (5)
19 Line on a weather map (6)
21 Affirmative (3)
22 Mechanics (9)

Down

1 Chopping tool (3)
2 Happen (5)
3 Disregards (7)
4 Mental pictures (6)
5 Number (6)
7 Synthetic material (9)
8 Insect (9)
12 Part cut off (7)
14 Study (6)
15 Aromatic spice (6)
17 Love deeply (5)
20 Donkey (3)

Across

1 Light waterproof jacket (7)
5 Fizzy water (4)
7 Meadow (3)
8 Travelling fair (8)
9 Gangway (5)
10 Retain (4)
13 Old Testament book (4)
14 Plant part (4)
18 Sagacious (4)
19 Stand-in doctor (5)
21 Novice (8)
22 Be unwell (3)
23 Whip (4)
24 Missives (7)

Down

1 Blameworthy (8)
2 Boxing term (5,3)
3 Male relatives (6)
4 I have found it! (6)
5 Tarantula, say (6)
6 Costly (4)
11 Buy (8)
12 Place of great disorder (8)
15 End (6)
16 Herb type (6)
17 Red wine (6)
20 Second Greek letter (4)

33

Across

1 Dad (6)
4 Mr Armstrong, cyclist (5)
7 Specific (10)
8 Applaud (4)
9 Stupid pupil (5)
11 Vivid red (7)
13 Navigational instrument (7)
15 Sheds tears (5)
17 Scheme (4)
18 Reference book (10)
20 Time when dark (5)
21 Abrupt (6)

Down

1 Noisy quarrel (6)
2 Pile (4)
3 Revolves or spins (7)
4 Readily understood (5)
5 Nothing (3)
6 Weird (5)
7 Royal residence (6)
10 Almost (6)
12 Lockjaw (7)
14 Sinew (6)
15 Broaden (5)
16 Fast (5)
17 Poke (4)
19 Toothed wheel (3)

Across

1 Speeds up (11)
7 Hereditary unit (4)
8 Narrow fissure or crack (7)
9 Flightless bird (3)
10 Precipitation (5)
11 Bewail (6)
13 Pointed beard (6)
16 Roofing slabs (5)
18 Zodiac sign (3)
19 Word for word (7)
20 Destroy (4)
21 Candid (5-6)

Down

1 Schedule (6)
2 Dairy product (6)
3 Destructive insect (6)
4 Spools (5)
5 Spear with three prongs (7)
6 Ghost (7)
11 Allow to escape (3,4)
12 Civilian fighting force (7)
13 Horse's gait (6)
14 Waterproof jacket (6)
15 Naval flag (6)
17 Warning device (5)

35

Across

1 Flatfish (7)
7 Yearly (6)
8 Of the heart (7)
9 Visage (4)
10 Portent (4)
12 Traditional Irish game (7)
14 Swimmer's breathing tube (7)
16 Let it stand (4)
18 Gargantuan (4)
20 Igneous rock (7)
21 Pleasure craft (6)
22 Snuggles (7)

Down

1 Bullies (7)
2 Big (5)
3 French cheese (4)
4 Discreet (7)
5 Steals, informally (8)
6 Bird of prey (6)
11 Viking (8)
12 Six-sided figure (7)
13 Assembles (7)
15 Queasiness (6)
17 Coil (5)
19 Girl (4)

Across

1 Range of words (10)
6 Work up (6)
7 Slight colouring (5)
9 Claws (6)
10 Hiatus (3)
11 Mr Ferguson, football boss (4)
14 Norse god (4)
15 Acquire (3)
16 Secret, mysterious, etc. (6)
17 Unspoken (5)
18 Runs away to wed (6)
20 Resolute (10)

Down

1 Anger or annoy (3)
2 Culminating point (6)
3 Native of Brittany (6)
4 Most recent (6)
5 Traitor (8)
6 Edible snail (8)
8 Deletes or erases (8)
9 Feeler (8)
12 Baby's toy (6)
13 Shriek or shrill cry (6)
14 Lent out (2,4)
19 Finish (3)

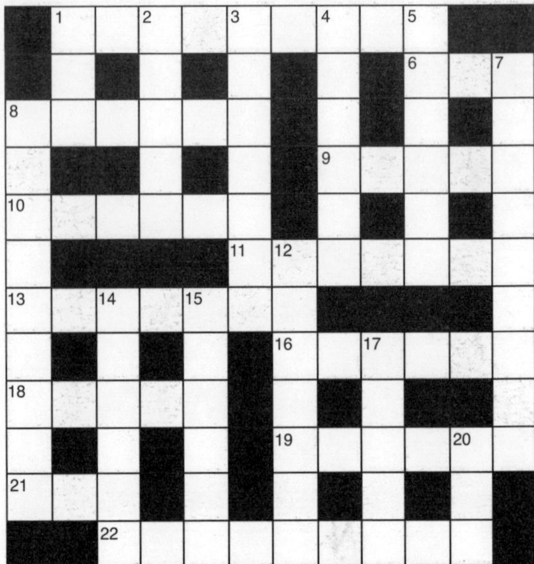

Across

1 Financial aspects (9)
6 Sound of disapproval (3)
8 Thin cord (6)
9 Circular coral reef (5)
10 Inn (6)
11 Whole number (7)
13 Move forward (7)
16 Rule (6)
18 Perfect (5)
19 Three times (6)
21 Religious sister (3)
22 Evaluators (9)

Down

1 Partake of food (3)
2 Oily fruit (5)
3 Fundamental (7)
4 Very young child (6)
5 Powerful (6)
7 Capacity to endure (9)
8 State of affairs (9)
12 Nullifies (7)
14 Austrian capital (6)
15 Stockings (6)
17 Zodiac sign (5)
20 Lettuce (3)

Across

1 Articles fit to eat (7)
5 Shove (4)
7 Summit (3)
8 Gifted (8)
9 Indian corn (5)
10 End part (4)
13 Sound quality (4)
14 Horse's gait (4)
18 Undiluted (4)
19 Governs (5)
21 Nazi emblem (8)
22 In favour of (3)
23 Burden (4)
24 Instance (7)

Down

1 Calculate roughly (8)
2 Lock up (8)
3 Second of two (6)
4 Cleaves (6)
5 An expert (6)
6 Pace (4)
11 Sweet on a stick (8)
12 Diamond, say (8)
15 Tantalises (6)
16 Hit (6)
17 Fleet of ships (6)
20 Mr McGregor, actor (4)

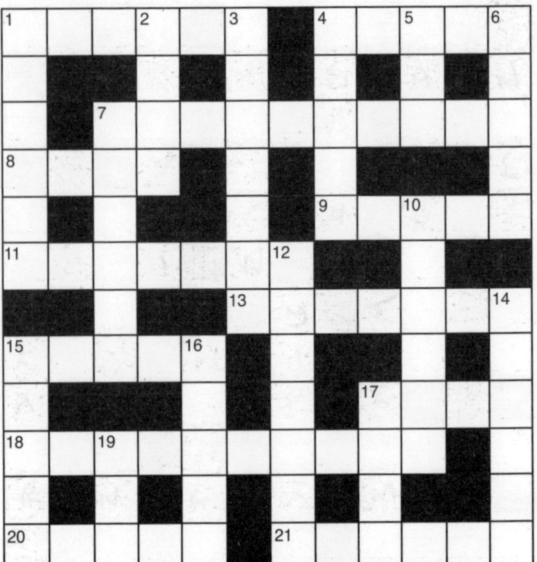

39

Across

1 To be precise (4,2)
4 Two-footed animal (5)
7 Level (10)
8 Give out cards (4)
9 Vast crowd (5)
11 Infectious disease (7)
13 Begins again (7)
15 Melts (5)
17 Ballet skirt (4)
18 Criminal (10)
20 Discourage (5)
21 Precious metal (6)

Down

1 Bicycle for two (6)
2 Implement (4)
3 Sly laugh (7)
4 Stall (5)
5 Container (3)
6 Rummage (5)
7 Cuban capital (6)
10 Gossip or hearsay (6)
12 Chooses (7)
14 Dazed state (6)
15 Timorous (5)
16 As yet (2,3)
17 Labour (4)
19 Auction item (3)

Across

1 Fruitless undertaking (5,6)
7 Revise (4)
8 Short axe (7)
9 Grief (3)
10 Stinks (5)
11 Rook (6)
13 Stroke lovingly (6)
16 Archery ring (5)
18 Angry crowd (3)
19 Remarkable (7)
20 Forearm bone (4)
21 At once (11)

Down

1 Hat type (6)
2 Get the better of (6)
3 Plot dishonestly (6)
4 Helicopter blade (5)
5 Attain (7)
6 Hates (7)
11 Italian wine (7)
12 Sacred or holy place (7)
13 Photographic device (6)
14 Reprove (6)
15 Thin (6)
17 Furious (5)

Across

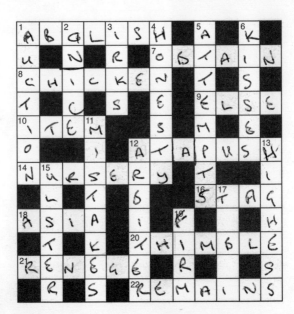

1 Do away with (7)
7 Acquire (6)
8 Fowl (7)
9 Otherwise (4)
10 Article (4)
12 With difficulty (2,1,4)
14 Crèche (7)
16 Male deer (4)
18 Continent (4)
20 Sewing aid (7)
21 Go back on one's word (6)
22 Part left over (7)

Down

1 Public sale (7)
2 In abeyance (2,3)
3 Annoys (4)
4 Truthfulness (7)
5 Tries (8)
6 Osculates (6)
11 Errors (8)
12 Referee (7)
13 Topmost (7)
15 Man's overcoat (6)
17 Shinbone (5)
19 Solid or stable (4)

Across

1 Do as others do (6,4)
6 Rupture (6)
7 Sleeve ends (5)
9 Distant (6)
10 Regret (3)
11 Courage and determination (4)
14 Chimney deposit (4)
15 Number (3)
16 Writer (6)
17 Hangman's halter (5)
18 Enlists (6)
20 Variety (10)

Down

1 Enemy (3)
2 Surgical knife (6)
3 Public speaker (6)
4 Holy (6)
5 Lower in value or quality (8)
6 Intensify (8)
8 Pullovers (8)
9 Harsh, severe, etc. (8)
12 Like instantly (4,2)
13 Road (6)
14 Origin (6)
19 Illuminated (3)

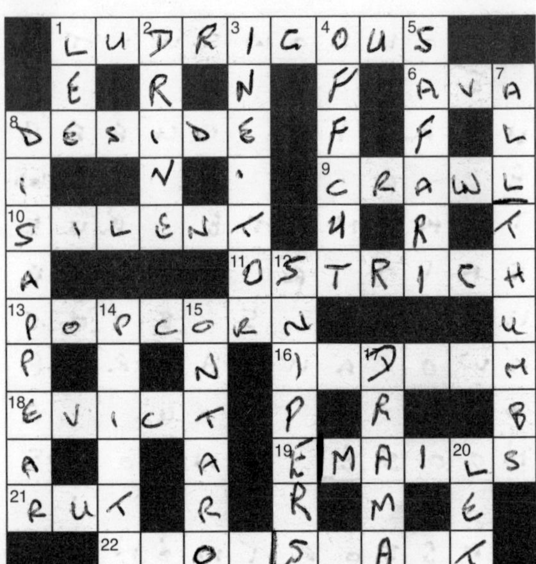

Across

1 Absurd (9)
6 __ Gardner, actress (3)
8 Determine (6)
9 Swimming stroke (5)
10 Noiseless (6)
11 Fast-running bird (7)
13 Cinema snack (7)
16 Metallic element (6)
18 Turn out (5)
19 Electronic messages (1-5)
21 Groove (3)
22 Initial advantage (4,5)

Down

1 Sheltered side (3)
2 Ambition (5)
3 Originator (7)
4 Remnant (6)
5 Jungle expedition (6)
7 Clumsy, informally (3,6)
8 Vanish (9)
12 Hidden gunmen (7)
14 Base (6)
15 Capital of Canada (6)
17 Play (5)
20 Permit (3)

44

Across

1 Flagrant, unashamed, etc. (7)
5 Gaelic (4)
7 Signal agreement (3)
8 Fish (8)
9 Bury (5)
10 Only remaining (4)
13 Greek spirit (4)
14 Use one's eyes (4)
18 Neck part (4)
19 Heavenly messenger (5)
21 Beekeeper (8)
22 Faucet (3)
23 One time (4)
24 Peculiar (7)

Down

1 Very lazy (4,4)
2 Screen test (8)
3 Respect highly (6)
4 Equipment (6)
5 Nevertheless (4,2)
6 Cast off (4)
11 Wolfram (8)
12 Fall in (8)
15 Martial art (6)
16 Starts (6)
17 Pancake mix (6)
20 Rotate (4)

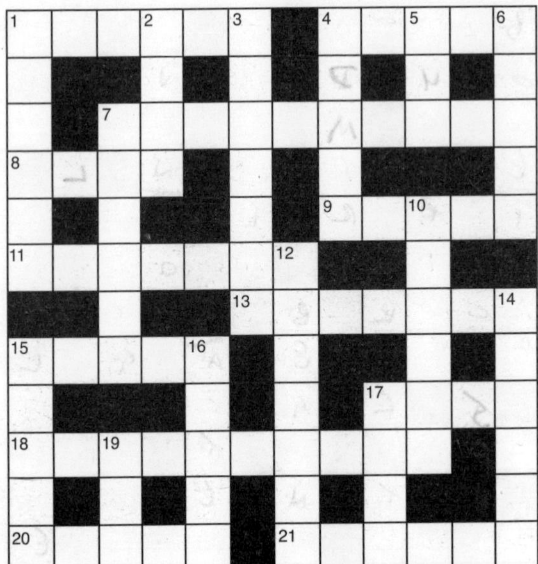

Across

1 Lowest point (6)
4 English town (5)
7 Chastises (10)
8 Halt (4)
9 Of birth (5)
11 Vocalists (7)
13 Crocus (7)
15 Fundamental (5)
17 Body powder (4)
18 A considered opinion (10)
20 Doctrine (5)
21 Rota (6)

Down

1 Ruptures (6)
2 Snare (4)
3 Shooting stars (7)
4 Truck (5)
5 Acquired (3)
6 Of the nose (5)
7 Enumerates (6)
10 Sikh's headdress (6)
12 Stroll (7)
14 Drink of the gods (6)
15 Rear (5)
16 Punctuation mark (5)
17 Fling (4)
19 Label (3)

Across

1 Journey's end (11)
7 Leg joint (4)
8 Acrobat's bar (7)
9 Expert (3)
10 Play for time (5)
11 Small cupboard (6)
13 Vouchers (6)
16 Beast of burden (5)
18 Diocese (3)
19 Foreboding evil (7)
20 Freshwater fish (4)
21 Basic (11)

Down

1 Of the teeth (6)
2 Large scissors (6)
3 Purpose (6)
4 Accumulate (5)
5 Repeat (7)
6 Knitting rods (7)
11 Cancel or abandon (4,3)
12 Prolonged applause (7)
13 Struggle (6)
14 Persevere or persist in (4,2)
15 Metallic element (6)
17 Pleasant smell (5)

47

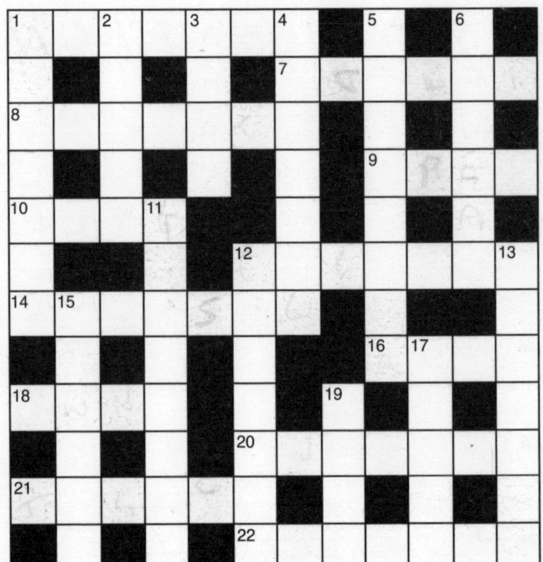

Across

1 American state (7)
7 Excused (6)
8 Underground cell (7)
9 Female relative (4)
10 Sharpen (4)
12 Table game (7)
14 Entourage (7)
16 Dutch cheese (4)
18 Golf club (4)
20 In pieces (7)
21 Bowed stringed instrument (6)
22 Spartan (7)

Down

1 Bereaved husband (7)
2 Snow leopard (5)
3 Notion (4)
4 Authentic (7)
5 Much less (3,5)
6 Light cake (6)
11 Three-sided figure (8)
12 Seedless raisin (7)
13 Repentance (7)
15 Insect (6)
17 Sidestep (5)
19 Ado (4)

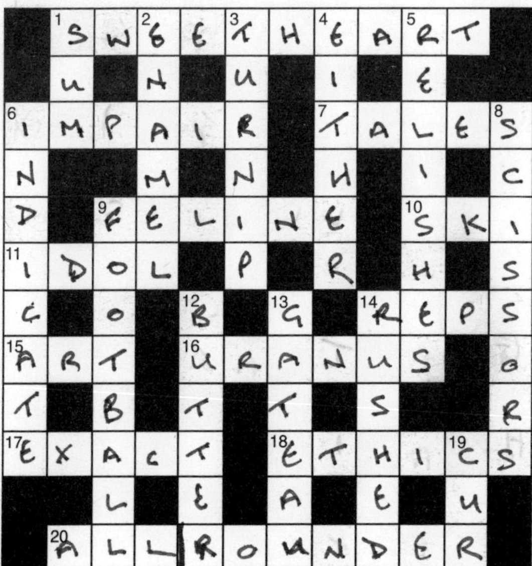

Across

1 True love (10)
6 Damage or weaken (6)
7 Stories (5)
9 Of cats (6)
10 Snow runner (3)
11 Object of worship (4)
14 Agents (4)
15 Skill (3)
16 Planet (6)
17 Precise (5)
18 Moral principles (6)
20 Versatile cricketer (3-7)

Down

1 Total (3)
2 Tooth covering (6)
3 Root vegetable (6)
4 One or the other (6)
5 Savours (8)
6 Point out or show (8)
8 Cutting instrument (8)
9 Sport (8)
12 Dairy product (6)
13 Fancy cake (6)
14 Hurried (6)
19 Mongrel (3)

49

Across

1 Accompaniment to lamb (4,5)
6 Hawaiian garland (3)
8 Run quickly (6)
9 Monetary unit (5)
10 In addition (2,4)
11 Component (7)
13 As a whole (2,5)
16 Foreign language (6)
18 Legal possessor (5)
19 Usual (6)
21 Towboat (3)
22 Amuse (9)

Down

1 Orienteering aid (3)
2 Simplistic (5)
3 Colonises (7)
4 False or incorrect (6)
5 Pass by like time (6)
7 Exactly alike (9)
8 Whipping boy (9)
12 Beginner (7)
14 Cope (6)
15 Rigorous (6)
17 Major artery (5)
20 Girl's name (3)

Across

1 Curtail (7)
5 Hop-drying kiln (4)
7 Spirit (3)
8 Drivel (8)
9 English city (5)
10 Close with a bang (4)
13 Locate (4)
14 Naming word (4)
18 Couple (4)
19 Concur (5)
21 Disparage (8)
22 Wrath (3)
23 Exaggerated publicity (4)
24 Game of chance (7)

Down

1 __ Jolie, actress (8)
2 Person finishing 2nd (6-2)
3 Of Denmark (6)
4 Mr Hemingway, writer (6)
5 Musical dramas (6)
6 Mediocre (2-2)
11 Headache (8)
12 Graveyard (8)
15 Indigenous (6)
16 Cruel or vicious (6)
17 Dormant (6)
20 Extremely (4)

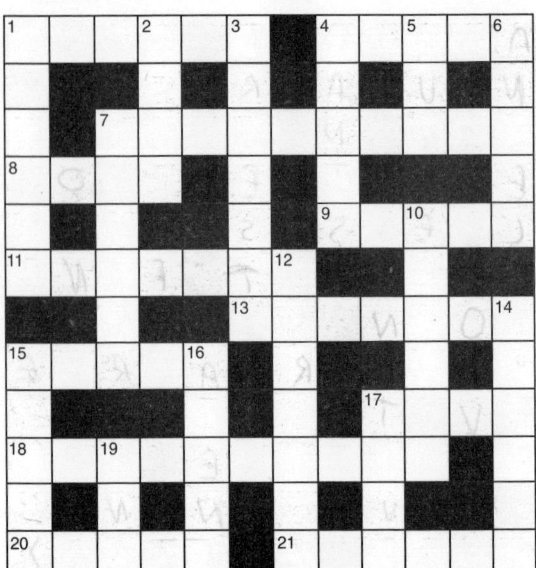

Across

1 Nearly (3,3)
4 Cheroot, say (5)
7 Board game (10)
8 Warmth (4)
9 Cutlery item (5)
11 Forage crop (7)
13 Liberty (7)
15 Inexpensive (5)
17 Worry (4)
18 Nourishing (10)
20 Eagle's nest (5)
21 Tray (6)

Down

1 Respiratory disorder (6)
2 Unruly child (4)
3 Become airborne (4,3)
4 Scorches (5)
5 Adhesive (3)
6 Mr Keating, singer (5)
7 Perplex (6)
10 Commands (6)
12 Axillae (7)
14 Parent (6)
15 Light boat (5)
16 Group of lions (5)
17 Complete (4)
19 Hill (3)

Across

1 Incomprehensible talk (6,5)
7 Unfortunately (4)
8 Meat-axe (7)
9 Epoch (3)
10 Wait on (5)
11 Cavort (6)
13 A sage (6)
16 Merchandise (5)
18 Close friend (3)
19 Pull out (7)
20 Unit of length (4)
21 Inconsiderate (11)

Down

1 Monetary unit (6)
2 Invisible (6)
3 Find (6)
4 Actions (5)
5 Greek restaurant (7)
6 Reap (7)
11 Colorant (7)
12 On the point of (5,2)
13 Group of seven (6)
14 Travelling case (6)
15 Female relatives (6)
17 Colloquial language (5)

53

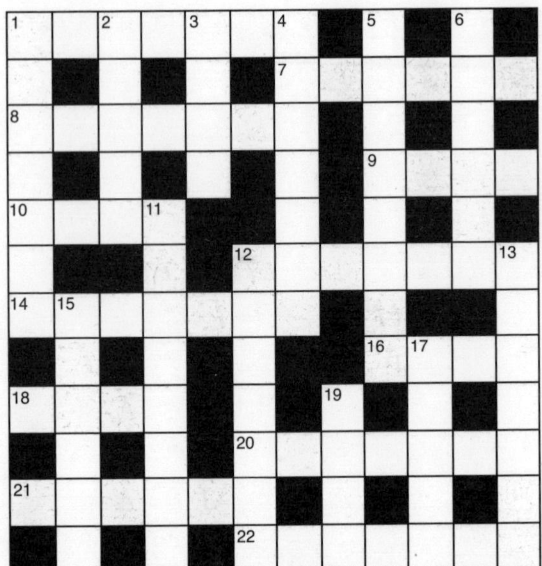

Across

1 Trade ban (7)
7 Glow-worm, say (6)
8 Modernises (7)
9 Corrode (4)
10 Mimics (4)
12 Make ready (7)
14 Even-tempered (7)
16 Golf pegs (4)
18 Arm or leg (4)
20 Operating room (7)
21 Funeral car (6)
22 Chorus (7)

Down

1 Teach (7)
2 Emblem (5)
3 Evaluate (4)
4 Vague (7)
5 Dilapidated (8)
6 Nearer (6)
11 Sword holder (8)
12 Conspirator (7)
13 Oriental (7)
15 Tremble (6)
17 Additional (5)
19 Red meat (4)

Across

1 Revolting (10)
6 Clergyman (6)
7 Proportion (5)
9 Grinding teeth (6)
10 Flipper (3)
11 First man (4)
14 Hairstyle (4)
15 Pitch (3)
16 Freshwater mammals (6)
17 School tests (5)
18 Beat (6)
20 Whirlybird (10)

Down

1 Female deer (3)
2 Situation comedy, in short (6)
3 Pandemonium (6)
4 Songbird (6)
5 Tells (8)
6 Witty retort (8)
8 Salve (8)
9 Wedding (8)
12 Japanese dwarf tree (6)
13 Artist's workroom (6)
14 Financial gain (6)
19 Ventilate (3)

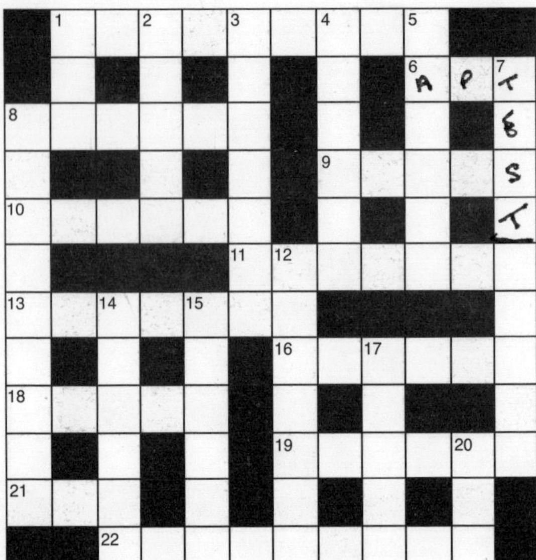

55

Across

1 English city (9)
6 Appropriate (3)
8 Showing kindliness (6)
9 Increases in size (5)
10 Summer, say (6)
11 Childish fit of rage (7)
13 Forsake (7)
16 Fare receipt (6)
18 Mournful song (5)
19 Entangle (6)
21 Fish eggs (3)
22 Warship (9)

Down

1 Falsehood (3)
2 Blood vessels (5)
3 Collide with (3,4)
4 Primary source (6)
5 Toil (6)
7 Cricket international (4,5)
8 Onlooker (9)
12 Aardvark (3,4)
14 Inflatable mattress (3,3)
15 Fears greatly (6)
17 Comfortable, informally (5)
20 Knight's title (3)

Across

1 Put into print (7)
5 Cold weather (4)
7 Consume (3)
8 Very hot curry (8)
9 Gambling odds (5)
10 Injure with a knife (4)
13 Standard (4)
14 Tightly stretched (4)
18 Heap (4)
19 Anaesthetic (5)
21 Hungarian capital (8)
22 Mr Gibson, actor (3)
23 Eyelid inflammation (4)
24 Wobbles (7)

Down

1 Gifts (8)
2 Flatter (6,2)
3 Put money in (6)
4 Trustworthy (6)
5 Mariner (6)
6 Musical instrument (4)
11 Exuberant friendliness (8)
12 Gemstones (8)
15 Declamation (6)
16 Polite and respectable (6)
17 Couch (6)
20 Search for prey (4)

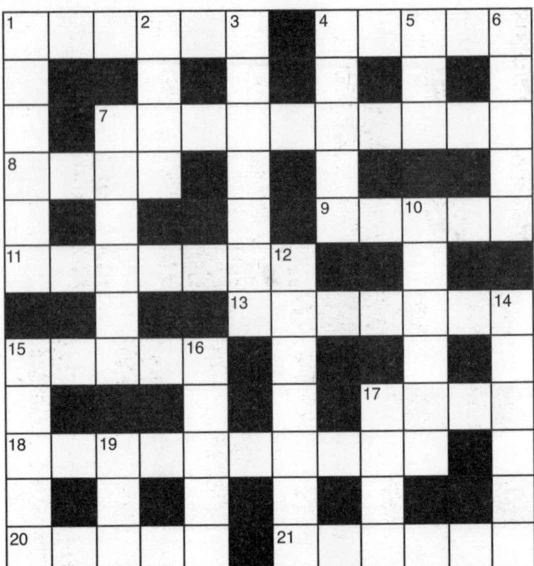

Across

1 Stationary (6)
4 Brimless cap (5)
7 Pirate flag (5,5)
8 Adjoin (4)
9 Rub out (5)
11 Optimistic (7)
13 Chipolata, say (7)
15 Feathered friends (5)
17 Perceive by touching (4)
18 Disgraceful (10)
20 Glasses, informally (5)
21 Naturist (6)

Down

1 Spatter (6)
2 Sound a horn (4)
3 Unfeeling (7)
4 Canal boat (5)
5 Floor covering (3)
6 Abrupt (5)
7 Upper garment (6)
10 Subsides (6)
12 Wool fat (7)
14 Join up (6)
15 Fundamental (5)
16 Flanks (5)
17 Money reserve (4)
19 Wonderment (3)

Across

1 Theatrical make-up (11)
7 Association of countries (4)
8 Chuckle gleefully (7)
9 Cigarette deposit (3)
10 Tattered fragment (5)
11 Passionate (6)
13 Peevish (6)
16 Gemstones (5)
18 Unwell (3)
19 Whaler's spear (7)
20 Egg-shaped (4)
21 Firework (5,6)

Down

1 Nick Faldo, say (6)
2 Get away (6)
3 Shampoo pouch (6)
4 Godly (5)
5 Temporary or provisional (7)
6 Weekday (7)
11 One more (7)
12 Drawing (7)
13 Former coin (6)
14 Remove cargo from (6)
15 Roof of the mouth (6)
17 Derision (5)

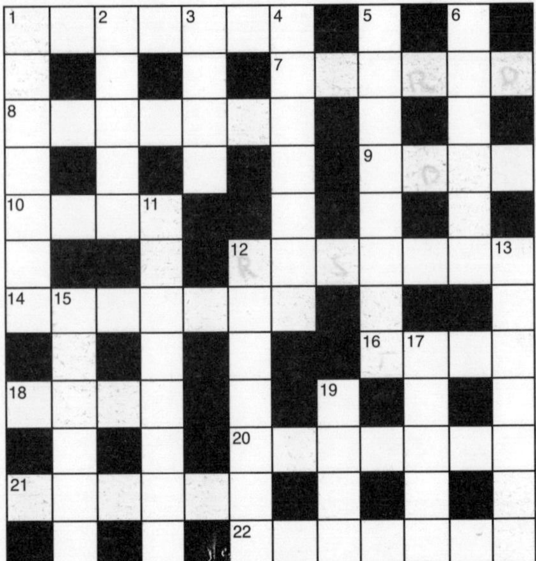

59

Across

1 Tedium (7)
7 Skilful or dexterous (6)
8 Catches fire (7)
9 Lash (4)
10 Drawn matches (4)
12 Medium (7)
14 Difficult to catch (7)
16 Written words (4)
18 Lazy (4)
20 Friendly (7)
21 Stopped (6)
22 To see (7)

Down

1 Easily broken (7)
2 Wash out (5)
3 Romantic appointment (4)
4 Exceptionally large (7)
5 Rodent (5,3)
6 Norseman (6)
11 State of anxious uncertainty (8)
12 Fruit (7)
13 Immoderate (7)
15 Stocking run (6)
17 Cinder (5)
19 Snake's sound (4)

Across

1 Explosive device (6,4)
6 Season (6)
7 Eskimo house (5)
9 Sharp bend (6)
10 Signal agreement (3)
11 Lord (4)
14 Miserly (4)
15 Viewing organ (3)
16 Branched horn (6)
17 Large ferocious fish (5)
18 Hardly ever (6)
20 Bolsters (10)

Down

1 Circuit (3)
2 Maker of menswear (6)
3 Swallow up (6)
4 River crossing (6)
5 Swing the lead (8)
6 Plugs or bungs (8)
8 Common or garden (8)
9 Depute (8)
12 Serviette (6)
13 Hi-fi (6)
14 Of measurement (6)
19 __ Dennis, comedian (3)

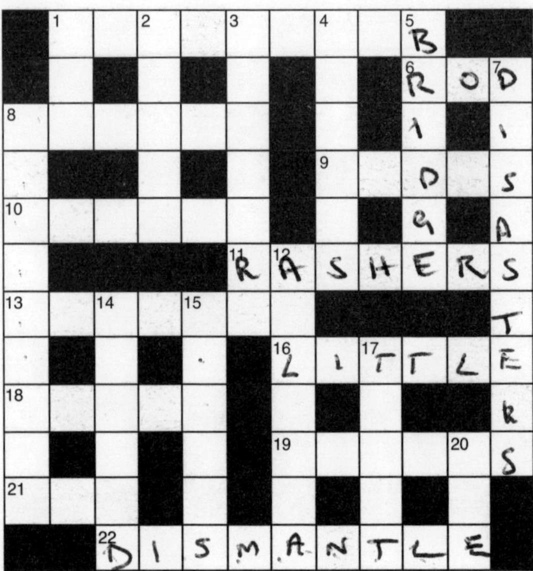

Across

1 Widespread (9)
6 Fish (3)
8 Instant (6)
9 Lasses (5)
10 Kitchen device (6)
11 Bacon slices (7)
13 Imply (7)
16 Small (6)
18 Picture within another (5)
19 Cloud type (6)
21 Foot digit (3)
22 Take apart (9)

Down

1 Personal pride (3)
2 English river (5)
3 Chatters (7)
4 Mental pictures (6)
5 Card game (6)
7 Calamities (9)
8 Temporary substitute (9)
12 American city (7)
14 Panted (6)
15 Goes in (6)
17 Entice (5)
20 Employ (3)

Across

1 Scientists (7)
5 Boat of logs (4)
7 Wildebeest (3)
8 Without socks or shoes (8)
9 Complete (5)
10 Volition (4)
13 Nobleman (4)
14 Broad smile (4)
18 Short letter (4)
19 Representative (5)
21 Irish emblem (8)
22 Perish (3)
23 Soon (4)
24 Gives up work (7)

Down

1 Resent (8)
2 Jet of water (8)
3 Congenital (6)
4 Canny (6)
5 Type of lottery (6)
6 Amphibian (4)
11 Pale bluish-purple colour (8)
12 Flaps (8)
15 Boy's name (6)
16 Eat voraciously (6)
17 Parcel (6)
20 Leg part (4)

63

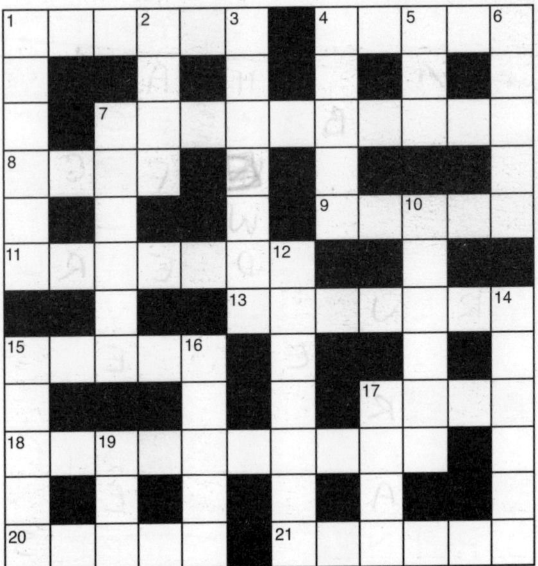

Across

1 Mohair (6)
4 Ring-shaped roll (5)
7 Loud confused noise (10)
8 Lyric poems (4)
9 Tugs (5)
11 Except for (7)
13 Tot (7)
15 Fashion (5)
17 Simple card game (4)
18 Whimsical (10)
20 Express gratitude to (5)
21 Assemble (6)

Down

1 Soak up (6)
2 Burden (4)
3 Minor illness (7)
4 Policeman, informally (5)
5 Congeal (3)
6 Plunders (5)
7 Funeral car (6)
10 Stockings (6)
12 Young goose (7)
14 Mend (6)
15 Unspoken (5)
16 Beverage (5)
17 Fat used in cooking (4)
19 Vegetable (3)

Across

1 Leaving no trace behind (4,4,3)
7 Clenched hand (4)
8 Duck type (7)
9 Container (3)
10 Of the kidneys (5)
11 Develop into (6)
13 Rank (6)
16 Severe or intense (5)
18 Newt (3)
19 Tennis officials (7)
20 Competent (4)
21 A game (11)

Down

1 Frozen spike (6)
2 Military pageant (6)
3 Fall awkwardly (6)
4 Loafer (5)
5 Versus (7)
6 Conundrums (7)
11 Cookie (7)
12 Applauded (7)
13 Playground item (6)
14 Accomplish (6)
15 Male relatives (6)
17 Danger (5)

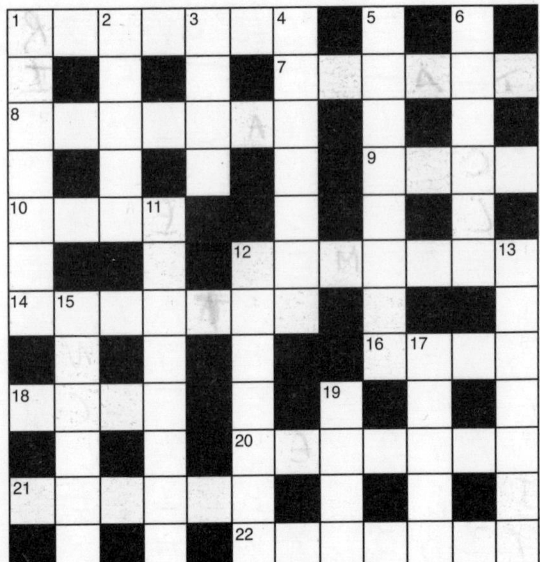

Across

1 Destructive insects (7)
7 Cutlery items (6)
8 Confidential (7)
9 Defensive ditch (4)
10 Mosque prayer leader (4)
12 Spectre (7)
14 Clear a path! (7)
16 Lather (4)
18 Heroic (4)
20 Planet (7)
21 Vicious (6)
22 Kings, queens, etc. (7)

Down

1 Green plover (7)
2 Country (5)
3 Remain (4)
4 Superficial or slight (7)
5 Card suit (8)
6 Pleasure craft (6)
11 Conjuror (8)
12 Ally or companion (7)
13 Enigma (7)
15 Seem or look (6)
17 Customary (5)
19 Active and brisk (4)

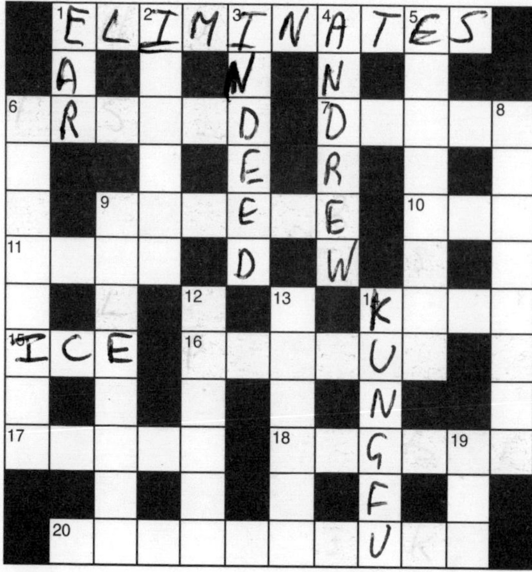

Across

1 Wipes out (10)
6 Terrain (6)
7 Considers (5)
9 Expunge (6)
10 Gardening implement (3)
11 Prayer ending (4)
14 Make woollens (4)
15 Frozen water (3)
16 Still batting (3,3)
17 American city (5)
18 Heathens (6)
20 An urge to travel (10)

Down

1 Hearing organ (3)
2 Insight (6)
3 Certainly (6)
4 Mr Lloyd Webber, composer (6)
5 Pachyderm (8)
6 Cultivated plant (8)
8 Takes refuge (8)
9 Brown sugar (8)
12 Cruel (6)
13 Dazed state (6)
14 Martial art (4,2)
19 Mesh (3)

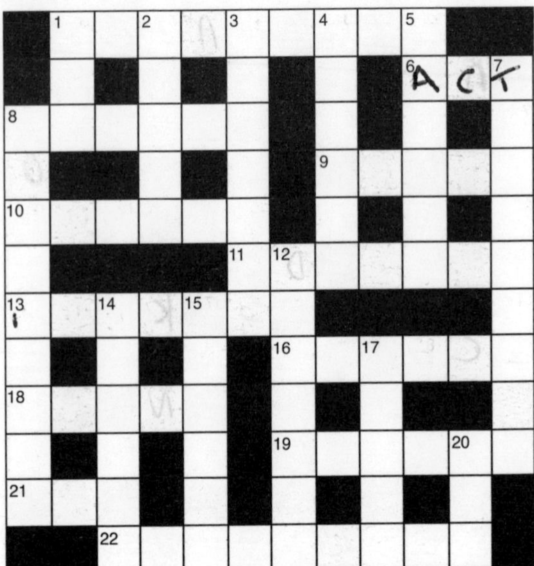

67

Across

1 In succession (2,3,4)
6 Perform on stage (3)
8 Protect (6)
9 Stadium (5)
10 Edge or frontier (6)
11 Acknowledges with praise (7)
13 Coach (7)
16 Baby's toy (6)
18 Existence (5)
19 Mettle (6)
21 Female sheep (3)
22 As it were (2,2,5)

Down

1 Mineral (3)
2 Tyre surface (5)
3 Sanction (7)
4 Recollect (6)
5 Ability (6)
7 Of short duration (9)
8 Moot (9)
12 Nabs (7)
14 Tolerates (6)
15 Lump of gold (6)
17 Two times (5)
20 Writing fluid (3)

Across

1 False belief (7)
5 Toddlers (4)
7 Skill (3)
8 One-storey house (8)
9 Stinks (5)
10 Go out (4)
13 Metal money (4)
14 African river (4)
18 Spun thread (4)
19 Free of obstruction (5)
21 Genealogy (8)
22 Slope downwards (3)
23 Remain (4)
24 Guided (7)

Down

1 Openly outrageous (8)
2 Recently (8)
3 Waylay (6)
4 Over there (6)
5 Mournful or pitiable (6)
6 An implement (4)
11 Bullfighter (8)
12 Fearless (8)
15 At a canter (6)
16 Sleeps noisily (6)
17 Agree (6)
20 Nuisance (4)

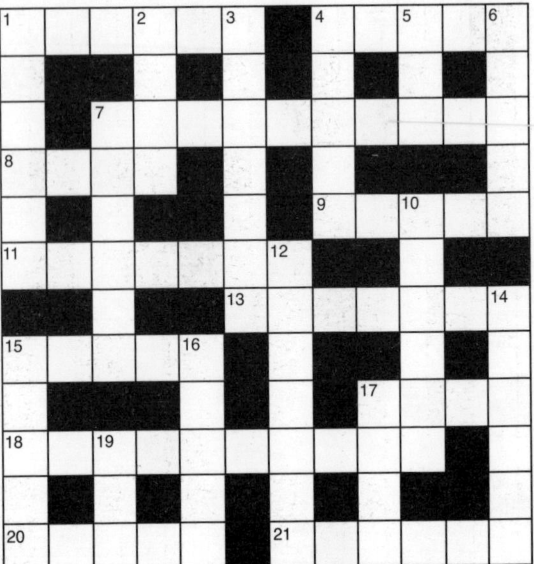

Across

1 Amongst (6)
4 Greek letter (5)
7 Bed type (4-6)
8 Man, informally (4)
9 Country (5)
11 Staying power (7)
13 Judas (7)
15 Perfume (5)
17 Datum (4)
18 Added or supplementary (10)
20 Golf's Mr Els (5)
21 Sleazy (6)

Down

1 Counting frame (6)
2 Let fall (4)
3 Torture (7)
4 Twelve dozen (5)
5 Floor covering (3)
6 Pinafore (5)
7 Outward appearance (6)
10 Of the stars (6)
12 Strenuous (7)
14 Plump (6)
15 Garden tool (5)
16 Name (5)
17 Just (4)
19 Loud continuous noise (3)

Across

1 Tolerant in one's views (5-6)
7 Entreaty (4)
8 Golden syrup (7)
9 Definite article (3)
10 Noblemen (5)
11 Brags (6)
13 Season (6)
16 Recess (5)
18 Eisenhower's nickname (3)
19 Oblivious (7)
20 Wound mark (4)
21 Very pleased or amused (7,4)

Down

1 Spanish dance (6)
2 Addresses the public (6)
3 Discourages (6)
4 Perfect (5)
5 Propriety (7)
6 Kitchen sideboard (7)
11 Feast (7)
12 Ancient (7)
13 Protect or guard (6)
14 Breakfast food (6)
15 Board a ship (6)
17 Electronic message (1-4)

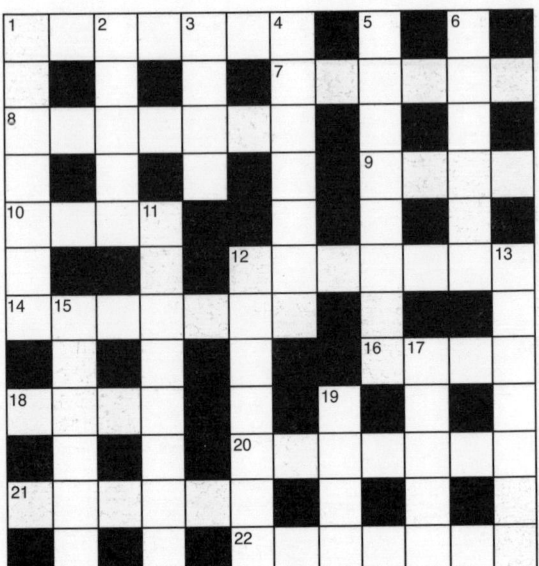

71

Across

1 Speaker's platform (7)
7 Eludes (6)
8 Dawdler (7)
9 Difficult (4)
10 Mines (4)
12 Inflatable rubber bag (7)
14 Everlasting (7)
16 Bring up (4)
18 Cooker (4)
20 Very large fire (7)
21 Belief (6)
22 Piercing screams (7)

Down

1 Return of ill health (7)
2 Vision (5)
3 Genuine (4)
4 Health-check (7)
5 Unmarried man (8)
6 Not far from (4,2)
11 Romantic song (8)
12 Brigands (7)
13 Jittery (7)
15 Inn (6)
17 Weird (5)
19 Way off (4)

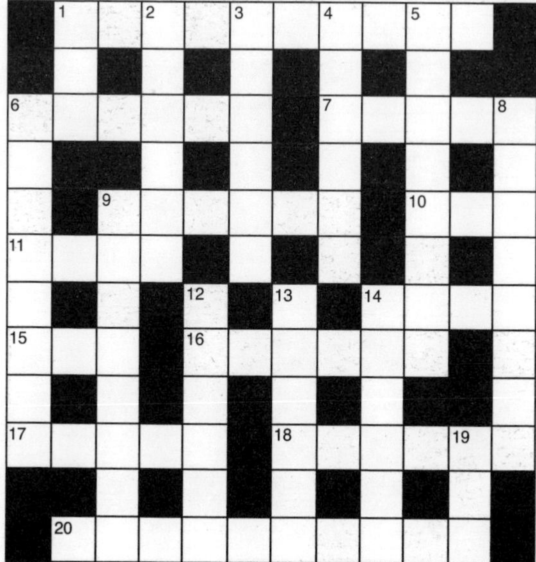

Across

1 Any desolate area (10)
6 Disregard (6)
7 Rotates (5)
9 Religious festival (6)
10 Prosecute (3)
11 Cod, for example (4)
14 Give food to (4)
15 Beverage (3)
16 Handsome young man (6)
17 Finger or toe (5)
18 Delicate or elegant (6)
20 Bolster (10)

Down

1 Hairpiece (3)
2 Back-scrubber (6)
3 Happenings (6)
4 Temperament (6)
5 Emphasises (8)
6 Doomed or unlucky (3-5)
8 Motorcycle sport (8)
9 Edible snail (8)
12 Combat (6)
13 Sausage in a long roll (3,3)
14 End (6)
19 Metallic element (3)

Across

1 Reckless (9)
6 Chew and swallow (3)
8 Prior to (6)
9 Emit light (5)
10 Joined (6)
11 Fundamental nature (7)
13 Refined (7)
16 Extremely (4,2)
18 Stage whisper (5)
19 Become aware of (6)
21 Faint (3)
22 Congregates (9)

Down

1 Owing (3)
2 Perch (5)
3 German city (7)
4 Against (6)
5 Injury or wound (6)
7 Thus (9)
8 Wide street or promenade (9)
12 Breastbone (7)
14 Mystery (6)
15 Representatives (6)
17 Exalt (5)
20 Lettuce (3)

1 2 3 4 5 6
7 8
9 10 11 12
13
14 15 16 17
18 19
20
21 22
23 24

Across

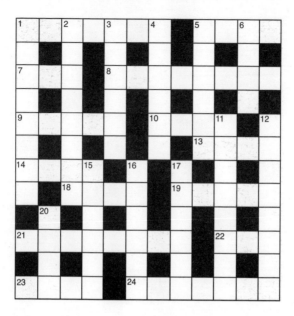

1 American city (7)
5 Greek letter (4)
7 Raised edge (3)
8 Supplementary part (8)
9 Deadly (5)
10 Corrosive substance (4)
13 Pleasant (4)
14 Deserve (4)
18 Facility (4)
19 Dutch cheese (5)
21 Dog (8)
22 Acquire (3)
23 Smile broadly (4)
24 Flow windingly (7)

Down

1 Having few worries (8)
2 Puerile (8)
3 Suitable for crops (6)
4 Difficult experience (6)
5 Interrupt (4,2)
6 Steady brisk pace (4)
11 Disclosed (8)
12 Stoppered bottle (8)
15 Incendiary liquid (6)
16 Average (6)
17 Schedule (6)
20 Run away (4)

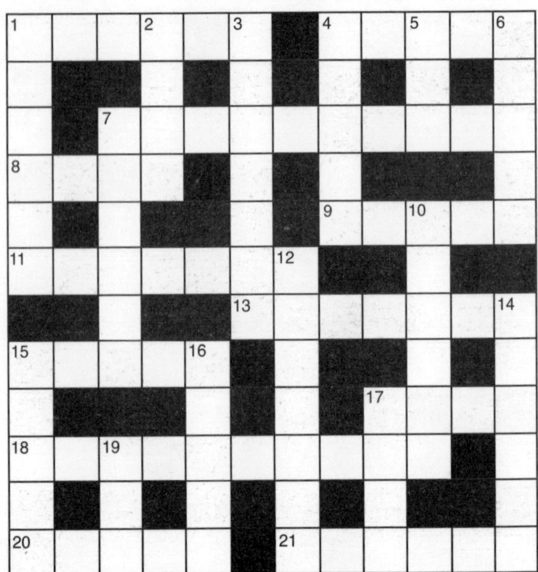

Across

1 Type of song (6)
4 Thin candle (5)
7 Charms (10)
8 Grain husks (4)
9 Lesson or lecture (5)
11 Coloured arc (7)
13 Not artificial (7)
15 Tree (5)
17 To bridge (4)
18 Large newspaper (10)
20 Water jugs (5)
21 Allow (6)

Down

1 Men's hairdresser (6)
2 Having no fat (4)
3 Ten-sided figure (7)
4 Garment (5)
5 Container (3)
6 Flowers (5)
7 Severe food shortage (6)
10 Curt (6)
12 Destroyer, say (7)
14 Surgical knife (6)
15 Holy book (5)
16 Conceals (5)
17 Scorch (4)
19 Number (3)

Across

1 Very early in the morning (5,2,4)
7 New Zealand bird (4)
8 Elfin creatures (7)
9 Total (3)
10 Surpass (5)
11 Mars, say (6)
13 Is irresolute (6)
16 Land measures (5)
18 Brazilian city, in short (3)
19 Unplaced horse (4-3)
20 Heavy metal (4)
21 Shabby (11)

Down

1 Hand tool (6)
2 Girl's name (6)
3 Fate or destiny (6)
4 Power (5)
5 Item (7)
6 Snuggles (7)
11 Poster (7)
12 Spray can (7)
13 Cautioned (6)
14 Bluish-purple colour (6)
15 Observe steadily (6)
17 Watch band (5)

77

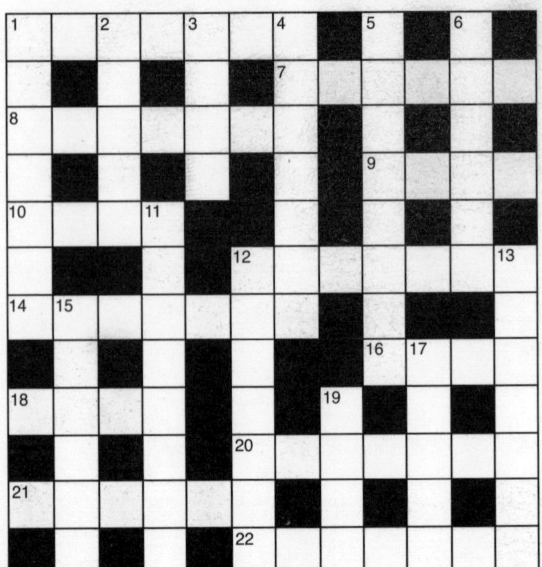

Across

1 Display (7)
7 Fits out (6)
8 Biggest (7)
9 Make beer (4)
10 Jetty (4)
12 Long-lasting (7)
14 Foes (7)
16 Podium (4)
18 Engrave (4)
20 Not either (7)
21 Ill-fated (6)
22 Surgical stitches (7)

Down

1 Surpass (7)
2 Equine mammal (5)
3 Red meat (4)
4 Lockjaw (7)
5 Storage place (8)
6 Ask earnestly (6)
11 Win a race easily (4,4)
12 Requests forcibly (7)
13 Guarantees (7)
15 Idea (6)
17 Detest vehemently (5)
19 Thin fog (4)

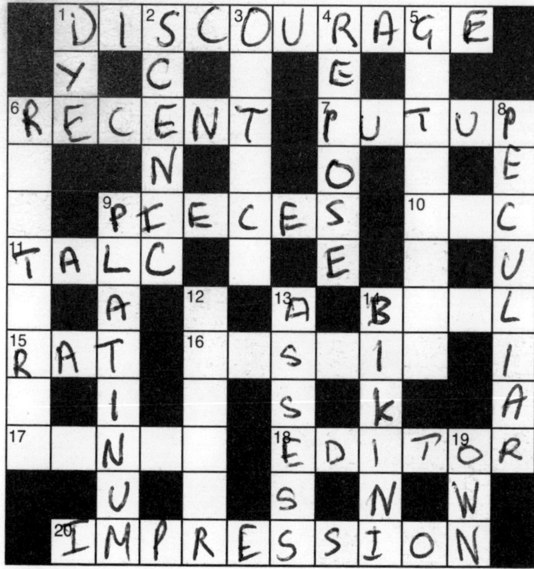

Across

1 Demoralise (10)
6 From the near past (6)
7 Build (3,2)
9 Bits (6)
10 Legendary bird (3)
11 Body powder (4)
14 Surety (4)
15 Rodent (3)
16 Descend by rope (6)
17 Light boat (5)
18 Newspaper boss (6)
20 Impersonation (10)

Down

1 Colorant (3)
2 Picturesque (6)
3 Tempt (6)
4 Peace or tranquillity (6)
5 Outer (8)
6 Oratory (8)
8 Strange (8)
9 Precious metal (8)
12 Move swiftly along (6)
13 Evaluate (6)
14 Swimming costume (6)
19 Possess (3)

79

Across

1 Extortion by threats (9)
6 Little devil (3)
8 Naval flag (6)
9 Chambermaid's workplace (5)
10 Sheep's wool (6)
11 Bewails (7)
13 Admit (7)
16 Highly-spiced sausage (6)
18 Sea duck (5)
19 Pressing (6)
21 Golf peg (3)
22 Onlooker (9)

Down

1 Forbid (3)
2 Burning (5)
3 Boarding place for dogs (7)
4 Song of praise (6)
5 Lend an ear (6)
7 Garment (4,5)
8 Competent (9)
12 Assail (7)
14 Pushes gently (6)
15 Provoke to fury (6)
17 Easy to lift (5)
20 And not (3)

Across

1 Competence (7)
5 Bushy hairstyle (4)
7 Biblical priest (3)
8 Long hot spell (4,4)
9 Speak slowly (5)
10 Produces eggs (4)
13 Mediocre (2-2)
14 Viewing organs (4)
18 Go by boat (4)
19 Clan (5)
21 Strength contest (3-2-3)
22 Vase (3)
23 Prophet (4)
24 Trailblazer (7)

Down

1 Scottish city (8)
2 Mimics (8)
3 Breathe in (6)
4 Annual (6)
5 On every occasion (6)
6 Party, slang (4)
11 State of being alone (8)
12 Prison chief (8)
15 Relish (6)
16 Explode (4,2)
17 Hi-fi (6)
20 Gargantuan (4)

81

Across

1 World or universe (6)
4 Courageous (5)
7 Hard to please (10)
8 Throw of dice (4)
9 Vestige (5)
11 Furry pet (7)
13 Merciful or tolerant (7)
15 Manner (5)
17 Japanese wrestling (4)
18 Unavoidable (10)
20 Wooden shoe (5)
21 Disburse (6)

Down

1 House of God (6)
2 Repast (4)
3 School bag (7)
4 Bathroom fitting (5)
5 Fuss (3)
6 Follow (5)
7 Light and thin (6)
10 Broad street (6)
12 Let go (7)
14 Sounded a horn (6)
15 Rotates (5)
16 Turn out (5)
17 Smack (4)
19 Flow away (3)

Across

1 Lights up (11)
7 Ado (4)
8 Patterns on a zebra (7)
9 Habitual drunkard (3)
10 Wear away (5)
11 Flag (6)
13 Small cupboard (6)
16 Group of eight (5)
18 Speck (3)
19 Brother or sister (7)
20 Den (4)
21 Compromise with (4,7)

Down

1 Lizard (6)
2 Period of instruction (6)
3 Overcome (6)
4 Courage (5)
5 Walks softly (7)
6 Dubious (7)
11 Bloom (7)
12 Remarkable or distinguished (7)
13 Blunt weapon (6)
14 Ban (6)
15 Bad blood (6)
17 Leg part (5)

83

Across

1 Antelope (7)
7 Almost (6)
8 Amidst (7)
9 Cupid (4)
10 Sudden blast of wind (4)
12 Malady (7)
14 Charming (7)
16 Towboats (4)
18 Desire (4)
20 Inactivity (7)
21 Spool (6)
22 Level of command (7)

Down

1 Scottish city (7)
2 Rushes (5)
3 Lower limbs (4)
4 Allow (7)
5 Filbert (8)
6 Gives out (6)
11 Laboratory vessel (4,4)
12 Picture mentally (7)
13 Withstand (7)
15 One after the other (2,1,3)
17 Up to the time of (5)
19 Net (4)

Across

1 Gymnastic feat (10)
6 Mild (6)
7 Wanderer (5)
9 Grief or deep sadness (6)
10 Sound of disapproval (3)
11 Paradise (4)
14 Stitched (4)
15 Choose (3)
16 Zodiac sign (6)
17 Soft leather (5)
18 Congenital (6)
20 Paper, pens, etc. (10)

Down

1 Gardening tool (3)
2 Country (6)
3 Fortified wine (6)
4 Fame (6)
5 Regardless of (2,6)
6 Open-handed (8)
8 Set off (8)
9 Strap worn in a car (4,4)
12 Stress or emphasis (6)
13 Spectral colour (6)
14 Spiritualists' meeting (6)
19 Rugby score (3)

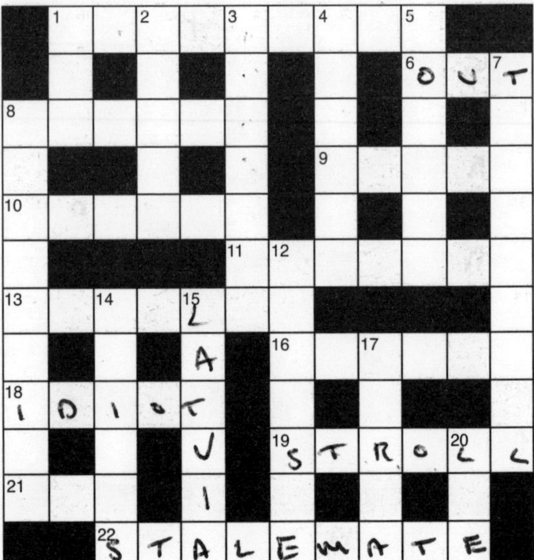

Across

1 Infamous (9)
6 Not at home (3)
8 Return to custody (6)
9 Lift (5)
10 Medical centre (6)
11 Takes for granted (7)
13 Kneecap (7)
16 Suds (6)
18 Fool (5)
19 Walks without hurrying (6)
21 Nothing (3)
22 Deadlock (9)

Down

1 Born (3)
2 Coach (5)
3 Fundamental (7)
4 Musical dramas (6)
5 Silvery-white element (6)
7 Cherishes (9)
8 Post-wedding function (9)
12 Save from destruction (7)
14 Coils (6)
15 European country (6)
17 Shinbone (5)
20 Biblical woman (3)

Across

1 Push down (7)
5 German wine (4)
7 Regret (3)
8 Refinement (8)
9 Processed meat (5)
10 Drawn matches (4)
13 Not any (4)
14 Religious sisters (4)
18 Sound quality (4)
19 Cake decoration (5)
21 Handcuffs (8)
22 Wager (3)
23 Foot covering (4)
24 Occidental (7)

Down

1 German city (8)
2 With child (8)
3 Badge (6)
4 Afternoon nap (6)
5 Concealed (6)
6 Traffic marker (4)
11 Convivial (8)
12 Intensify (8)
15 Comfort in distress (6)
16 Colour (6)
17 Osculates (6)
20 Ready money (4)

87

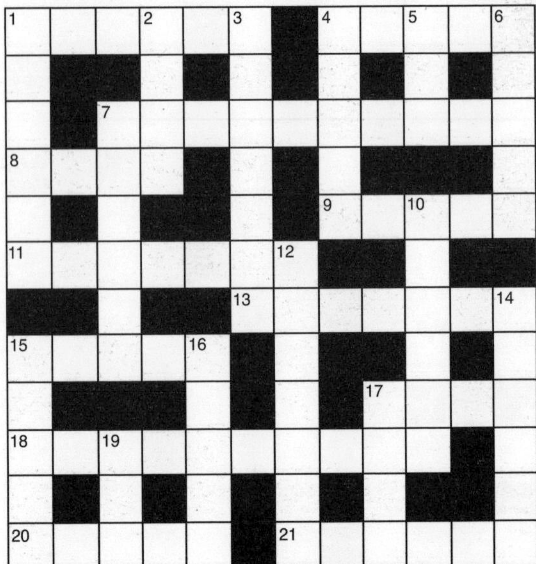

Across

1 Reviewer (6)
4 Precipitation (5)
7 Elaborate or extravagant (10)
8 Cain's brother (4)
9 Happen again (5)
11 Unprofessional (7)
13 Kelp, say (7)
15 Stealing (5)
17 Untidy state (4)
18 At all (10)
20 Monetary unit (5)
21 Sensitive (6)

Down

1 Country (6)
2 Plough (4)
3 Cloud type (7)
4 Animal's trail (5)
5 Epoch (3)
6 Private teacher (5)
7 Of a woman (6)
10 Intelligent (6)
12 Admiration (7)
14 Cleaning cloth (6)
15 Turret (5)
16 Flavour (5)
17 Intend (4)
19 Venomous snake (3)

Across

1 Crabby (3-8)
7 Make things with wool (4)
8 Collide with (3,4)
9 Hand tool (3)
10 Pursuit (5)
11 Swoons (6)
13 Equipment (6)
16 Fertile spot (5)
18 Harden (3)
19 Chooses (7)
20 Horses (4)
21 Naval vessel (11)

Down

1 Fruit (6)
2 Delay or hold back (6)
3 Exit (6)
4 Sudden fear (5)
5 Plunder (7)
6 Bishop's district (7)
11 Wreckage found floating (7)
12 Pancreatic hormone (7)
13 Struggle (6)
14 Light sleep (6)
15 Lumberjack (6)
17 Cults (5)

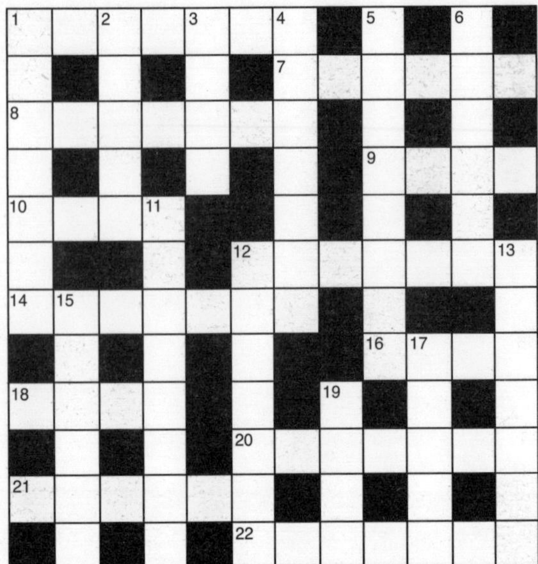

89

Across

1 Spear (7)
7 Musical (6)
8 Listening carefully (3,4)
9 Expel (4)
10 Betting chances (4)
12 Particles of cut wood (7)
14 Confidentiality (7)
16 Roster (4)
18 Dull pain (4)
20 Easily broken (7)
21 Divulge (6)
22 Ambassador's residence (7)

Down

1 Green-eyed (7)
2 Based on truth (5)
3 Unauthorised disclosure (4)
4 Posy (7)
5 Disarray (8)
6 Population count (6)
11 Wizard or magician (8)
12 Tussle (7)
13 Type of play (7)
15 Go beyond (6)
17 Leaves out (5)
19 Young sheep (4)

Across

1 Toy weapon (10)
6 Pass a disease to (6)
7 Tubby (5)
9 Drinking toast (6)
10 In the past (3)
11 Notion (4)
14 Quick or furtive look (4)
15 Lyric poem (3)
16 Pressed clothes (6)
17 Push (5)
18 Marionette (6)
20 Generally (2,3,5)

Down

1 Play on words (3)
2 ___ Franklin, singer (6)
3 Intense dislike (6)
4 Be against (6)
5 Learned (8)
6 American state (8)
8 Explore for gold (8)
9 Formal act or ritual (8)
12 Bird (6)
13 To force (6)
14 Condiment (6)
19 Female sheep (3)

91

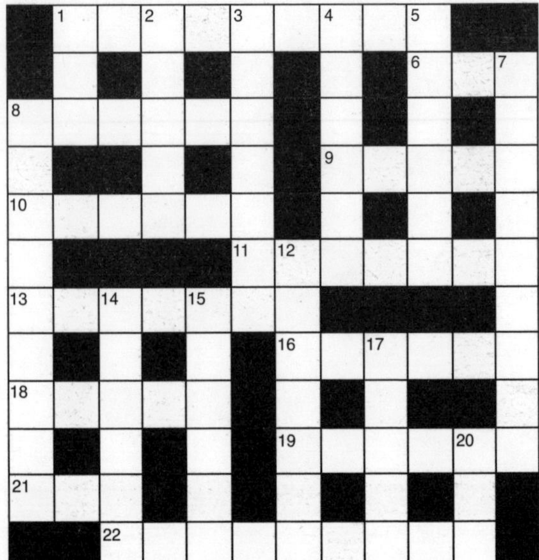

Across

1 Playwright (9)
6 Hairpiece (3)
8 Discard (6)
9 ____ MacArthur, yachtswoman (5)
10 Sinew (6)
11 Chatters (7)
13 According to reason (7)
16 Pointed beard (6)
18 Amid (5)
19 Decrees (6)
21 Ovum (3)
22 Immoderate (9)

Down

1 Perish (3)
2 In front (5)
3 Feeler (7)
4 Create or devise (6)
5 Dozen (6)
7 Violent criminals (9)
8 Hit back (9)
12 African city (7)
14 Mr Clooney, actor (6)
15 High-quality brandy (6)
17 Defence plea (5)
20 Foot part (3)

Across

1 Whim (7)
5 Ballet skirt (4)
7 Donkey (3)
8 Crucial (8)
9 Indicate (5)
10 Whip (4)
13 Roof slab (4)
14 Make eyes at (4)
18 Unit of length (4)
19 Foot-lever (5)
21 Target centre (5-3)
22 Rowing blade (3)
23 Therefore (4)
24 Scolds harshly (7)

Down

1 Supporter (8)
2 Perhaps or maybe (8)
3 Stir up (6)
4 Esculent (6)
5 Desire to drink (6)
6 Snare (4)
11 Furthest back (8)
12 States emphatically (8)
15 Birds of prey (6)
16 Part of speech (6)
17 Seem or look (6)
20 Shove (4)

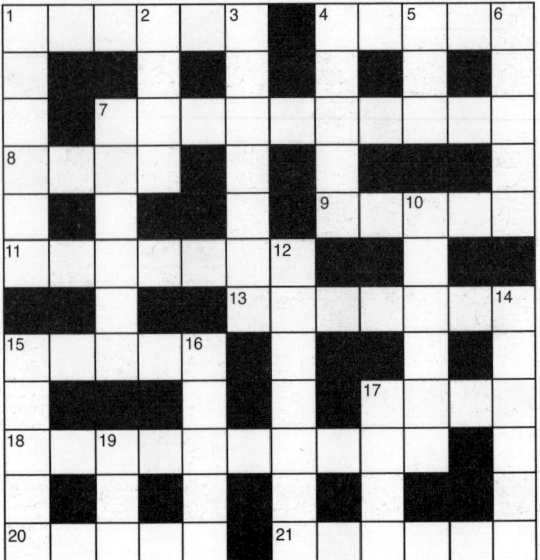

93

Across

1 Beer type (6)
4 Perspire (5)
7 Rank-and-file members (5,5)
8 Salver (4)
9 Stocky (5)
11 Rats, say (7)
13 Break into pieces (7)
15 Musical instrument (5)
17 Rich soil (4)
18 Occasionally (3,3,4)
20 Swiftness (5)
21 Tell (6)

Down

1 Pancake mix (6)
2 Conservative (4)
3 Withstands (7)
4 Rub hard (5)
5 Personal pride (3)
6 Snappish (5)
7 Land adjoining a house (6)
10 Fixed allowance (6)
12 Abbreviate (7)
14 Cure (6)
15 Long seat (5)
16 Snow leopard (5)
17 Departed (4)
19 Used to be (3)

Across

1 Approve automatically (6-5)
7 Drop (4)
8 Tooth expert (7)
9 Falsehood (3)
10 Colour (5)
11 Solution (6)
13 Humour (6)
16 Melts (5)
18 Knight's title (3)
19 Dismiss from consideration (4,3)
20 Young female (4)
21 Sensible (4-2-5)

Down

1 Motive (6)
2 Roar (6)
3 Make beloved (6)
4 Tendon (5)
5 Obstinate or stupid (7)
6 Earthenware (7)
11 Changed (7)
12 Having little depth (7)
13 Rook (6)
14 Amalgamation (6)
15 Scarcity (6)
17 To fire (5)

95

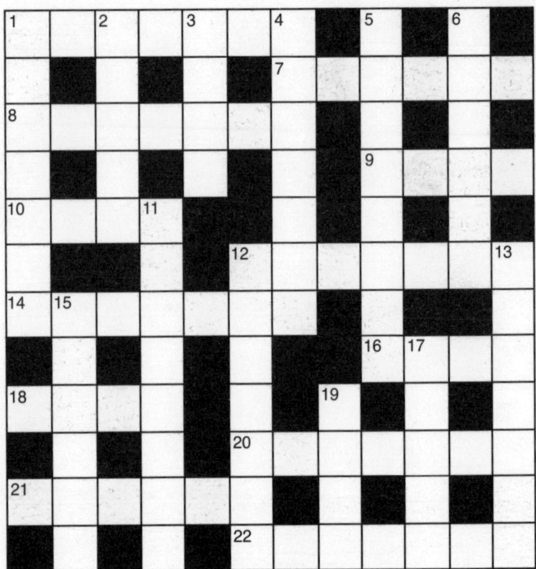

Across

1 Below (7)
7 Take no notice of (6)
8 Spring back (7)
9 Too (4)
10 Yes votes (4)
12 Opposite of failure (7)
14 Abducts (7)
16 Shock or overwhelm (4)
18 Object of worship (4)
20 Nourish (7)
21 Save (6)
22 Sharp reply (7)

Down

1 To jeer (7)
2 Sublime (5)
3 Fever (4)
4 Extremely ugly (7)
5 Improves (8)
6 Emergency (6)
11 Skin protection (8)
12 Hand tool (7)
13 Open and genuine (7)
15 Certainly (6)
17 Ruffians (5)
19 Excursion (4)

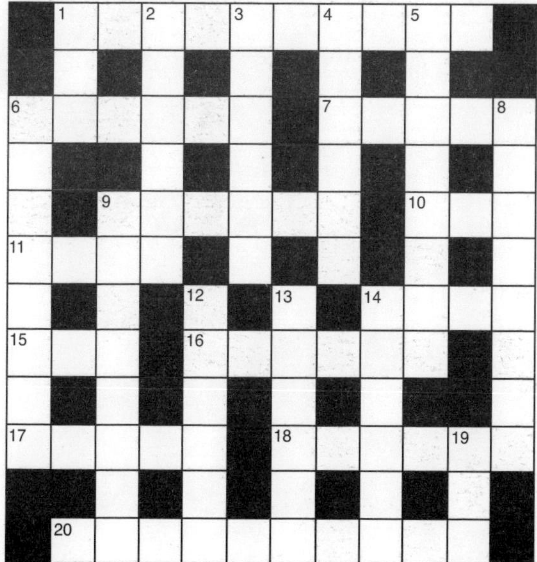

Across

1 Basis (10)
6 Perfect society (6)
7 Flowers (5)
9 Light wind (6)
10 Fish eggs (3)
11 Monster (4)
14 Bird's home (4)
15 Adult male (3)
16 Editions (6)
17 Of birth (5)
18 From one side to the other (6)
20 Soon (6,4)

Down

1 Seizure (3)
2 Tennis official (6)
3 Dealer in fabrics (6)
4 Objective (6)
5 Watches carefully (8)
6 Rare (8)
8 Ghosts (8)
9 Brown-haired woman (8)
12 Market or exchange (6)
13 Landed property (6)
14 Not far from (4,2)
19 Droop (3)

Across

1 Done at once (9)
6 Moo (3)
8 Slim and delicate (6)
9 Mr Blaine, magician (5)
10 Wall pass (3-3)
11 Concentrated (7)
13 Defile (7)
16 Glowered (6)
18 School tests (5)
19 Use (6)
21 Body of water (3)
22 Unbelieving (9)

Down

1 Unwell (3)
2 Power or force (5)
3 American city (7)
4 Amongst (6)
5 Number (6)
7 Weekday (9)
8 Latest news (4,5)
12 Lack of proper care (7)
14 South American mammals (6)
15 Of bears (6)
17 Savoury jelly (5)
20 Lubricate (3)

Across

1 Wheedles (7)
5 Strong wind (4)
7 Floor covering (3)
8 Abide (8)
9 Grab (5)
10 Norse god (4)
13 Abel's brother (4)
14 Plunder (4)
18 Organ of smell (4)
19 Exclusive (5)
21 Spring flower (8)
22 Expert (3)
23 Hereditary unit (4)
24 Sincere (7)

Down

1 Woman's under-bodice (8)
2 Throw overboard (8)
3 Untidy refuse (6)
4 Lounge (6)
5 Pungent bulb (6)
6 Plenty (4)
11 Plot a course (8)
12 Borrowing charge (8)
15 Chewy sweet (6)
16 Sewing implement (6)
17 Underground room (6)
20 Rescue (4)

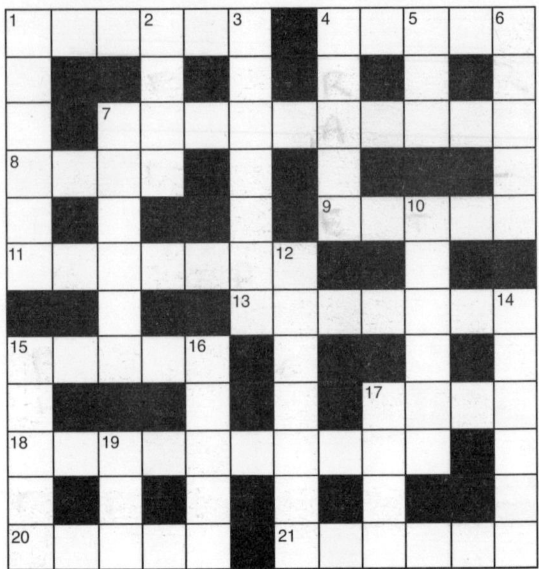

99

Across

1 Capricious (6)
4 Quotes (5)
7 Systematic (10)
8 Jump (4)
9 Very strong person (5)
11 Small crown (7)
13 Fruit (7)
15 Soft sweet (5)
17 Search for prey (4)
18 Emboldens (10)
20 Monk's costume (5)
21 Rubble (6)

Down

1 Gambol (6)
2 Retain (4)
3 Breathes out (7)
4 Military trainee (5)
5 Facial twitch (3)
6 Hairdresser's shop (5)
7 Spain's capital (6)
10 Zodiac sign (6)
12 Drinking vessel (7)
14 Thespians (6)
15 Newly made (5)
16 Burst out (5)
17 Parsley, say (4)
19 Loaf type (3)

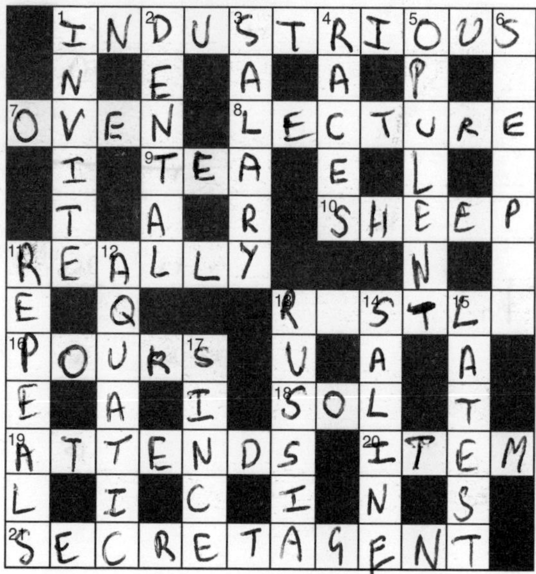

Across

1 Hard-working (11)
7 Cooker part (4)
8 Instructive discourse (7)
9 Hot drink (3)
10 Woolly animal (5)
11 Truly (6)
13 Steal cattle (6)
16 Rains heavily (5)
18 Mr Campbell, footballer (3)
19 Is present at (7)
20 Article (4)
21 Spy (6,5)

Down

1 Ask along (6)
2 Of the teeth (6)
3 Monthly pay (6)
4 Speed contests (5)
5 Abundant or plentiful (7)
6 Spire (7)
11 Revokes (7)
12 Of water (7)
13 Country (6)
14 Salty (6)
15 Most recent (6)
17 Because (5)

Across

1 Rifle attachment (7)
7 Loves deeply (6)
8 Slow and steady (7)
9 Heal (4)
10 Information (4)
12 Farewell (7)
14 Ruin (7)
16 Sully (4)
18 Water jug (4)
20 Infectious disease (7)
21 Sturdy walking shoe (6)
22 Office workers (7)

Down

1 Iraqi capital (7)
2 Raising agent (5)
3 Naming word (4)
4 Furniture item (7)
5 Admits defeat in (8)
6 Double-cross (6)
11 A second self (5,3)
12 Gastronome (7)
13 Joins up (7)
15 Mr Fox, actor (6)
17 Eyes up (5)
19 Lighting device (4)

Across

1 Completely (10)
6 Powerful (6)
7 Perch (5)
9 Sport (6)
10 Single number (3)
11 Look lasciviously (4)
14 Matted fabric (4)
15 Definite article (3)
16 Dealer or merchant (6)
17 Sound (5)
18 Runs away to wed (6)
20 Place to dine (10)

Down

1 Appropriate (3)
2 Tobacco user (6)
3 Myth (6)
4 Beat soundly (6)
5 Examine (4,4)
6 Set of bones (8)
8 Playhouses (8)
9 Put on TV (8)
12 Road (6)
13 Fancy cake (6)
14 Hat type (6)
19 Newt (3)

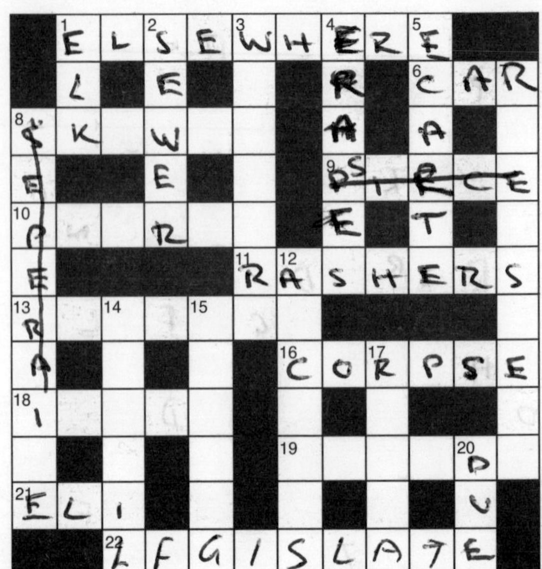

103

Across

1 In another place (9)
6 Vehicle (3)
8 Kebab spike (6)
9 Fragment (5)
10 ___ Estefan, singer (6)
11 Bacon slices (7)
13 Permits or tolerates (7)
16 Cadaver (6)
18 Performed on stage (5)
19 Wanderers (6)
21 Biblical priest (3)
22 Make laws (9)

Down

1 Moose (3)
2 Underground drain (5)
3 Conflict or strife (7)
4 Rubs out (6)
5 Card game (6)
7 Take back (9)
8 Set apart from others (9)
12 Climbs (7)
14 Particular (6)
15 A provocation (3,3)
17 Cuban dance (5)
20 Owing (3)

Across

1 Arrears of work (7)
5 Imitation (4)
7 Transgression (3)
8 Tortures (8)
9 Ingenuous (5)
10 Cummerbund (4)
13 Facility (4)
14 Wound mark (4)
18 Missing (4)
19 Multiplied by (5)
21 Burn without flame (8)
22 Flow away (3)
23 Let it stand (4)
24 Supervise (7)

Down

1 Trade or profession (8)
2 Man-eating human (8)
3 Missive (6)
4 Gaudy (6)
5 Dairy product (6)
6 Sympathy (4)
11 Innocuous (8)
12 Down-to-earth (8)
15 Sturdy (6)
16 Artist's workroom (6)
17 Deprive of food (6)
20 Discharge (4)

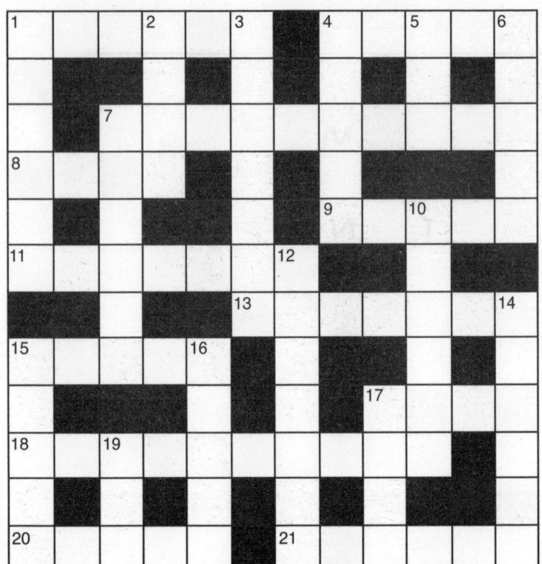

105

Across

1 Breed of small fowl (6)
4 Stinking (5)
7 Upside down (5-5)
8 Hang on (4)
9 Ancient language (5)
11 Expressionless (7)
13 Pantries (7)
15 Sugary (5)
17 English river (4)
18 Emphasises (10)
20 Fashion (5)
21 Rarely (6)

Down

1 Made beer (6)
2 Steady brisk pace (4)
3 Tuneful (7)
4 Ending in death (5)
5 Hill (3)
6 Senior member (5)
7 Declamation (6)
10 Topics (6)
12 Diapers (7)
14 Method (6)
15 Push to one side (5)
16 Weary (5)
17 Inform (4)
19 Female deer (3)

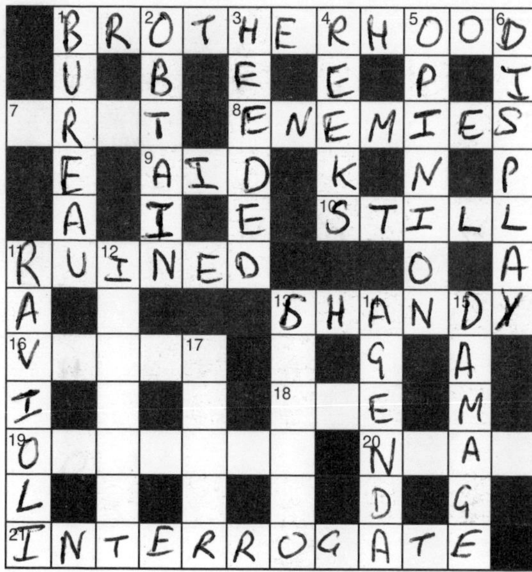

Across

1 Fraternity (11)
7 Worry (4)
8 Foes (7)
9 Help or assist (3)
10 Motionless (5)
11 Destroyed (6)
13 Beer with lemonade (6)
16 Changes direction (5)
18 Anger (3)
19 Prolonged applause (7)
20 Undiluted (4)
21 Question closely (11)

Down

1 Writing desk (6)
2 Acquire (6)
3 Took notice of (6)
4 Stinks (5)
5 Personal view (7)
6 Exhibit (7)
11 Italian food (7)
12 Imprecise (7)
13 Japanese religion (6)
14 Schedule (6)
15 Harm (6)
17 Winter sportsman (5)

107

Across

1 Flatfish (7)
7 Offensive (6)
8 Has in mind (7)
9 Christmas (4)
10 Hop-drying kiln (4)
12 Gift (7)
14 Sequin (7)
16 Fizzy water (4)
18 Forearm bone (4)
20 Extreme greed (7)
21 Pill (6)
22 Cost (7)

Down

1 Evil (7)
2 Water lily (5)
3 Loud explosion (4)
4 More than is required (2,5)
5 Musicians (8)
6 Adjust a radio (4,2)
11 Feeler (8)
12 Pacify (7)
13 Acrobat's bar (7)
15 Slender supporting column (6)
17 Edible bulb (5)
19 To pant (4)

Across

1 Gnu (10)
6 Thin cord (6)
7 Estimate (5)
9 Herb (6)
10 Cooker top (3)
11 Way off (4)
14 Unruly child (4)
15 Drawn match (3)
16 Bellowed (6)
17 Spools (5)
18 Ten years (6)
20 Jelly-like dessert (10)

Down

1 Rainy (3)
2 Linger (6)
3 Railway locomotive (6)
4 Swallow up (6)
5 One who tends sheep (8)
6 Unlawful occupant (8)
8 Deliberate destruction (8)
9 Goodbye (8)
12 Jail (6)
13 Haphazard (6)
14 Signal fire (6)
19 Scottish river (3)

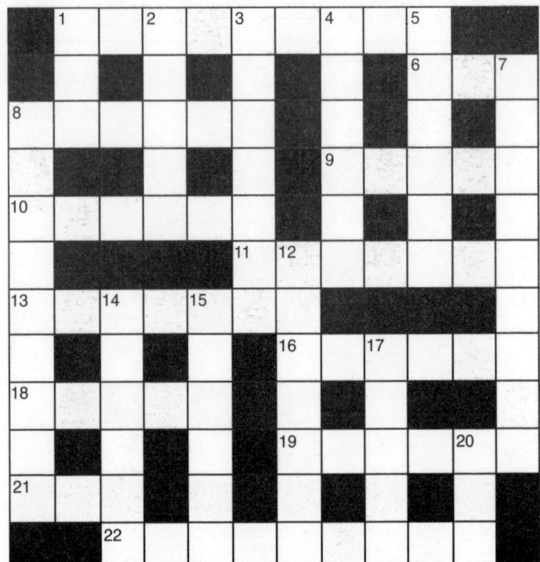

Across

1 Native practical intelligence (6,3)
6 Knock (3)
8 Wobble (6)
9 Search into closely (5)
10 Charm (6)
11 Catches fire (7)
13 Hug (7)
16 Idea (6)
18 Finnish bath (5)
19 Responds (6)
21 So or thus (3)
22 Moving staircase (9)

Down

1 __ West, actress (3)
2 Sum (5)
3 Irregular (7)
4 Gun, say (6)
5 Test (3,3)
7 Game birds (9)
8 Crosses (9)
12 Common (7)
14 Springiness (6)
15 Foreign language (6)
17 Characteristic (5)
20 Pitch (3)

Across

1 In name only (7)
5 Crease (4)
7 Fish (3)
8 Caution in practical affairs (8)
9 Slack (5)
10 Hotel cook (4)
13 Thick cord (4)
14 Stiff paper (4)
18 Gaelic (4)
19 Levy (5)
21 Think carefully about (8)
22 Ventilate (3)
23 Kill (4)
24 Determination (7)

Down

1 Jewellery item (8)
2 Second-rate (8)
3 Male relative (6)
4 Set afloat (6)
5 Tentacle (6)
6 Fortune (4)
11 Sport (8)
12 Practise (8)
15 Elegant (6)
16 Person in charge (6)
17 Begins (6)
20 Hair from sheep (4)

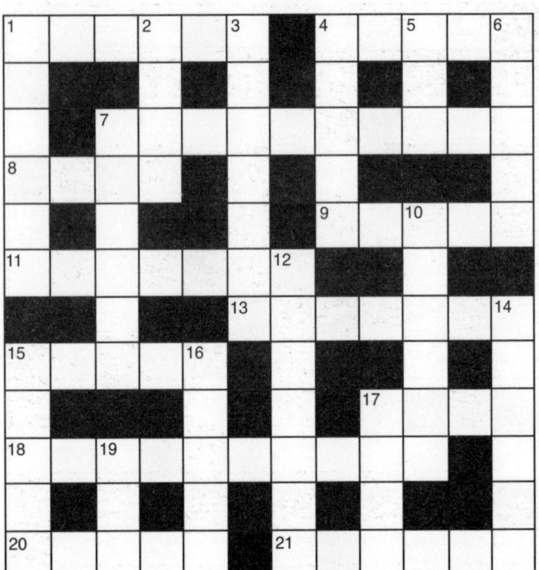

111

Across

1 Short fall of rain (6)
4 Stay clear of (5)
7 Aboriginal instrument (10)
8 Overwhelming defeat (4)
9 Actions (5)
11 Width (7)
13 Stroll (7)
15 Tries out (5)
17 Go by (4)
18 In prison (6,4)
20 Wash through (5)
21 Small mechanical device (6)

Down

1 Sacred beetle (6)
2 Legal document (4)
3 Rues (7)
4 Pungent (5)
5 Strange (3)
6 Worthless matter (5)
7 Coercion (6)
10 Crowd actors (6)
12 Woman's item (7)
14 Begrudge (6)
15 Italian river (5)
16 Scorch (5)
17 Poke (4)
19 Farmyard bird (3)

Across

1 Close together (5,2,4)
7 Couple (4)
8 Farm vehicle (7)
9 Consume (3)
10 Hangman's halter (5)
11 Martial art (6)
13 Place inside (6)
16 Young eel (5)
18 Dolt (3)
19 Funny drawing (7)
20 Corrosive substance (4)
21 Happy because of (7,4)

Down

1 Ballroom dance (3-3)
2 I have found it! (6)
3 Kitchen device (6)
4 Pine (5)
5 Result (7)
6 Biggest (7)
11 Patella (7)
12 Drive backwards (7)
13 Pressed (6)
14 Jungle expedition (6)
15 Pungent root (6)
17 Castles (5)

113

1		2		3		4		5		6	
						7					
8 S	T	O	M	A	C	H					
								9			
10			11								
					12						13
14	15										
								16	17		
18							19				
					20						
21											
					22						

Across

1 Clap (7)
7 Insight (6)
8 Belly (7)
9 Toddlers (4)
10 Plant ovule (4)
12 Make ready (7)
14 Facts and figures (7)
16 Verge (4)
18 Gemstone (4)
20 White ant (7)
21 Day nursery (6)
22 Draw back (7)

Down

1 Accumulated (7)
2 Military chaplain (5)
3 Land force (4)
4 Risks (7)
5 Having many parts (8)
6 Annoy continually (6)
11 Stalemate (8)
12 Coating for walls (7)
13 Component (7)
15 Specialist (6)
17 Ambition (5)
19 Gravel (4)

114

Across

1 Handicap (10)
6 Smells (6)
7 Educate (5)
9 Relegate (6)
10 Total (3)
11 Coagulate (4)
14 Genuine (4)
15 Tree type (3)
16 Monetary unit (6)
17 Ketchup, say (5)
18 Plays for time (6)
20 Incessantly repeated (10)

Down

1 Speck (3)
2 Sundown (6)
3 Chess piece (6)
4 Second of two (6)
5 Hand over (8)
6 School bags (8)
8 Having nowhere to live (8)
9 Small rodent (8)
12 Loafers (6)
13 Shuts (6)
14 Plunder (6)
19 Permit (3)

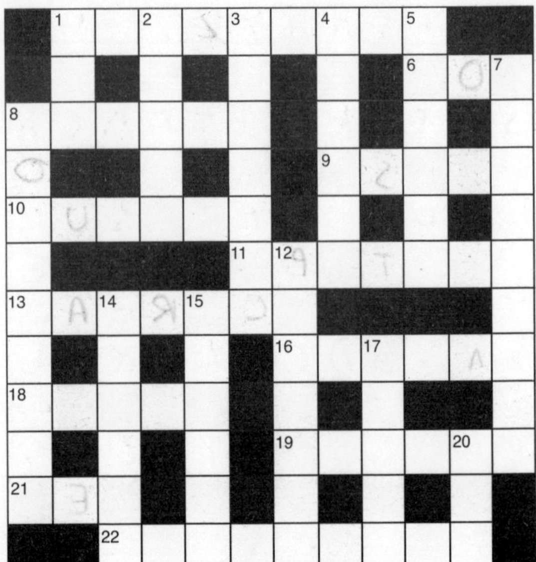

115

Across

1 Vaudeville (5,4)
6 Eisenhower's nickname (3)
8 Run quickly (6)
9 Detested (5)
10 Single-cell organism (6)
11 Medical practitioner (7)
13 Reap (7)
16 Eatable (6)
18 Furniture item (5)
19 Indian instruments (6)
21 Frozen water (3)
22 Detect something suspicious (5,1,3)

Down

1 Orienteering aid (3)
2 County (5)
3 Curved sword (7)
4 Fasten securely (6)
5 Small (6)
7 Imperils (9)
8 Form of pasta (9)
12 Tool or implement (7)
14 Gemstones (6)
15 Come into view (6)
17 Bury (5)
20 Groove (3)

Across

1 American state (7)
5 Long story (4)
7 Health resort (3)
8 Next day (8)
9 Allow to enter (3,2)
10 Condiment (4)
13 Public pool (4)
14 Labour (4)
18 Complain bitterly (4)
19 Perfect (5)
21 Mixed alcoholic drink (8)
22 Viewing organ (3)
23 Remain (4)
24 Truthfulness (7)

Down

1 Complete (8)
2 Slaughterhouse (8)
3 Temporary (6)
4 Very nearly (6)
5 Saunter (6)
6 Be incandescent (4)
11 Ageless (8)
12 Coal mine (8)
15 Servile follower (6)
16 Whiten (6)
17 Musical instrument (6)
20 Crossbow missile (4)

117

Across

1 Sags (6)
4 Salad garnish (5)
7 Burn up completely (10)
8 Hairpieces (4)
9 Bravery award (5)
11 Surgical knife (7)
13 Welsh rabbit (7)
15 Seat (5)
17 Amphibian (4)
18 Tedious (10)
20 Light beer (5)
21 World or universe (6)

Down

1 Speaks slowly (6)
2 Possesses (4)
3 Sea captain (7)
4 Top of milk (5)
5 Epoch (3)
6 Witch's formula (5)
7 Lizard type (6)
10 Excludes (6)
12 Terse (7)
14 Pantihose (6)
15 Desert animal (5)
16 Helicopter blade (5)
17 Ado (4)
19 Horse (3)

Across

1 Fairground ride (6,5)
7 Stout stick (4)
8 Part of a whole (7)
9 Egg cells (3)
10 Soft wet earth (5)
11 Bomb hole (6)
13 Venus, say (6)
16 Goes out (5)
18 Knight's title (3)
19 Place apart (7)
20 Chooses (4)
21 Clumsy (5-6)

Down

1 Waver (6)
2 Erase (3,3)
3 Damage or weaken (6)
4 Cautions (5)
5 Issue (7)
6 Merciful or tolerant (7)
11 Treasure (7)
12 American state (7)
13 Former monetary unit (6)
14 Overseas (6)
15 Very happy (6)
17 Frightening (5)

119

Across

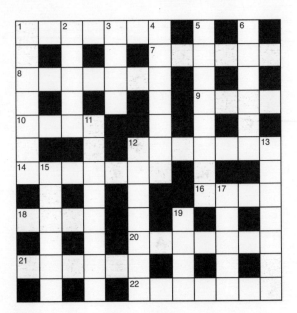

1 Jones, say (7)
7 Younger in years (6)
8 Remainder (7)
9 Operator (4)
10 Pig's grunt (4)
12 Six-sided figure (7)
14 Shocked (7)
16 Cupid (4)
18 Molten volcanic rock (4)
20 Everlasting (7)
21 Silky to the touch (6)
22 First batsmen (7)

Down

1 Thoughtful, solemn, etc. (7)
2 Tree sap (5)
3 Assistant (4)
4 Kicked out (7)
5 Move in waves (8)
6 Spanish dance (6)
11 Large marsupial (8)
12 Sailors' cry (5-2)
13 Snuggles (7)
15 Emotional shock (6)
17 Scope (5)
19 This place (4)

Across

1 Blue-veined cheese (10)
6 Kind and sympathetic (6)
7 Not ever (5)
9 Reverent (6)
10 Mesh (3)
11 Spur or incite (4)
14 Unable to hear (4)
15 Brick-carrier (3)
16 Writer (6)
17 Thin porridge (5)
18 Adjusts (6)
20 Shameless insolence (10)

Down

1 Wildebeest (3)
2 Wandered (6)
3 American state (6)
4 Highest point (6)
5 Pale bluish-purple (8)
6 Nocturnal mammal (8)
8 Gives formal consent to (8)
9 Scalp problem (8)
12 Seaman (6)
13 Accomplish (6)
14 Give (6)
19 Attempt (3)

121

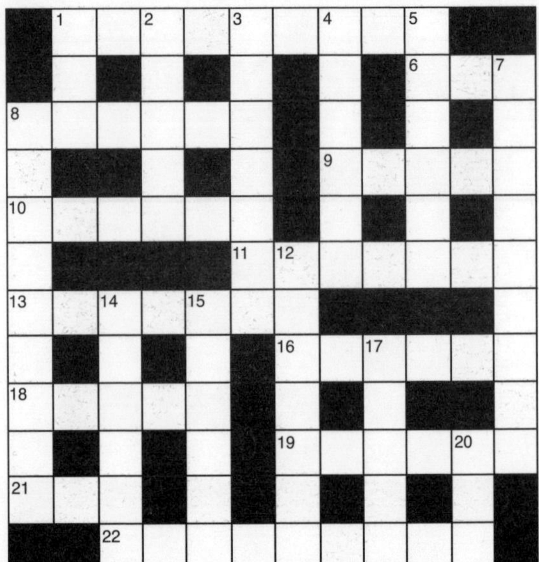

Across

1 Profitable (9)
6 Cease living (3)
8 Cloud type (6)
9 Thespian (5)
10 Stoat-like mammal (6)
11 Old soldier (7)
13 Artist (7)
16 System of self-defence (6)
18 Boy's name (5)
19 Turns out (6)
21 Legendary bird (3)
22 Of short duration (9)

Down

1 Garland of flowers (3)
2 Solid blocks (5)
3 Pardon (7)
4 Very young child (6)
5 Senior journalist (6)
7 Mistaken (9)
8 Publication (9)
12 Rubbers (7)
14 Untouched or unimpaired (6)
15 Albania's capital (6)
17 Cutlery item (5)
20 Sound of disapproval (3)

Across

1 Illegal (7)
5 Dairy product (4)
7 Illuminated (3)
8 Caribou (8)
9 Push (5)
10 Dull heavy noise (4)
13 Intend (4)
14 Coarse file (4)
18 Boy's name (4)
19 Bit (5)
21 Highest point (8)
22 Bend (3)
23 Hereditary unit (4)
24 Quite old (7)

Down

1 Deceptive or unreal (8)
2 Set free (3,5)
3 Floor covering (6)
4 Coils or spins (6)
5 Spiritualist (6)
6 Lecherous grin or sneer (4)
11 Month (8)
12 In progress (5,3)
15 Monarch's son (6)
16 Frozen spike (6)
17 Add (6)
20 Sagacious (4)

123

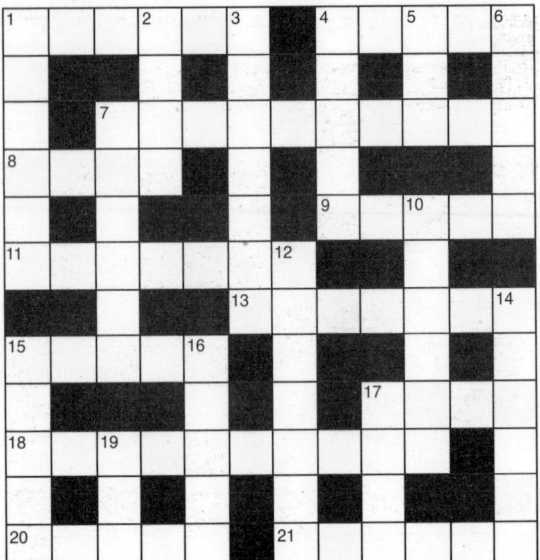

Across

1 Ember (6)
4 Schemes (5)
7 Current (7-3)
8 Tightly stretched (4)
9 Equine mammal (5)
11 Afternoon show (7)
13 Steal (7)
15 Flashlight (5)
17 French cheese (4)
18 Agreed suspension of activity (10)
20 Drainage channel (5)
21 Resounds (6)

Down

1 Business patronage (6)
2 Grime (4)
3 Begins again (7)
4 Party drink (5)
5 In addition to (3)
6 Manner (5)
7 Golf club (6)
10 Mend one's ways (6)
12 Sanction (7)
14 Happenings (6)
15 Timorous (5)
16 Emerge from an egg (5)
17 Shrub (4)
19 Rodent (3)

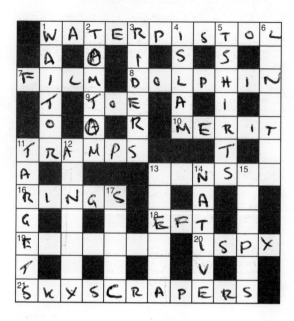

Across

1 Toy weapon (5,6)
7 Movie (4)
8 Marine mammal (7)
9 Foot digit (3)
10 Deserve (5)
11 Vagrants (6)
13 Perceives (6)
16 Jewellery items (5)
18 Newt (3)
19 Fundamental nature (7)
20 Guessing game (1-3)
21 Very tall buildings (11)

Down

1 Restaurant worker (6)
2 Drum type (3-3)
3 Jockeys (6)
4 Religion (5)
5 Upper garments (1-6)
6 Syrupy cough medicine (7)
11 Objectives (7)
12 General pardon (7)
13 ____ Easton, singer (6)
14 Indigenous (6)
15 Bursts out (6)
17 Of sound (5)

125

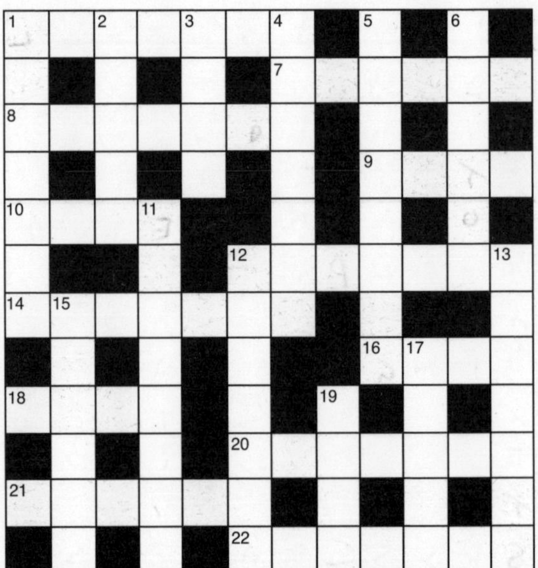

Across

1 Medium-sized monkeys (7)
7 Foundation garment (6)
8 Spite (7)
9 Expel (4)
10 Object of worship (4)
12 Versus (7)
14 A brief view (7)
16 Mexican snack (4)
18 Den (4)
20 Current of air (7)
21 Save (6)
22 Normal (7)

Down

1 Except for (7)
2 Housey-housey (5)
3 Musical instrument (4)
4 Miserly person (7)
5 Fire-raiser (8)
6 Population count (6)
11 Form of comic verse (8)
12 In pieces (7)
13 Pig's foot (7)
15 Yeast, say (6)
17 Heavenly messenger (5)
19 Suspend (4)

Across

1 Toad type (10)
6 Unlocked (6)
7 Sound (5)
9 Pleasure craft (6)
10 Anger (3)
11 Bring up (4)
14 Body powder (4)
15 Top card (3)
16 Beast (6)
17 Delightful surprise (5)
18 Tempt (6)
20 Astounding, wonderful, etc. (10)

Down

1 Card game (3)
2 Leather worker (6)
3 Make beloved (6)
4 Mr Button, racing driver (6)
5 Malefactor (8)
6 Cloudy (8)
8 Put into use (8)
9 Sidewalk (8)
12 Portable computer (6)
13 Racing bird (6)
14 Skin decoration (6)
19 Lettuce (3)

127

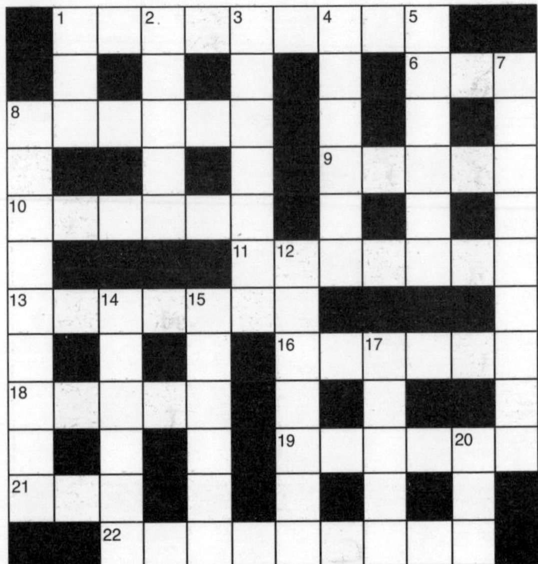

Across

1 Roller coaster (3,6)
6 Recede (3)
8 Celtic language (6)
9 Jewelled headdress (5)
10 Entertains (6)
11 Lewd (7)
13 Branch of maths (7)
16 Conundrum (6)
18 One who perseveres (5)
19 Takes on (6)
21 Female sheep (3)
22 Totally (3,4,2)

Down

1 Bleat (3)
2 Swallows eagerly (5)
3 Tooth (7)
4 Crockery items (6)
5 Deduction or discount (6)
7 Innocent (9)
8 Ensure (9)
2 Excellent buy (7)
14 Former coin (6)
15 Interment (6)
17 Lets fall (5)
20 Summit (3)

128

Across

1 Bullies (7)
5 Standard (4)
7 Fuss (3)
8 Business of government (8)
9 Follow (5)
10 Tightly stretched (4)
13 Remaining (2,2)
14 Untruths (4)
18 Twelve months (4)
19 Stinks (5)
21 Seven-sided figure (8)
22 Ventilate (3)
23 Active and brisk (4)
24 Playhouse (7)

Down

1 Celestial (8)
2 Chinese-style dish (4,4)
3 Fish-eating bird (6)
4 Military greeting (6)
5 Still batting (3,3)
6 Speed contest (4)
11 Permissive (8)
12 Preserve (8)
15 Soldier on guard (6)
16 Shining (6)
17 European country (6)
20 Pile (4)

129

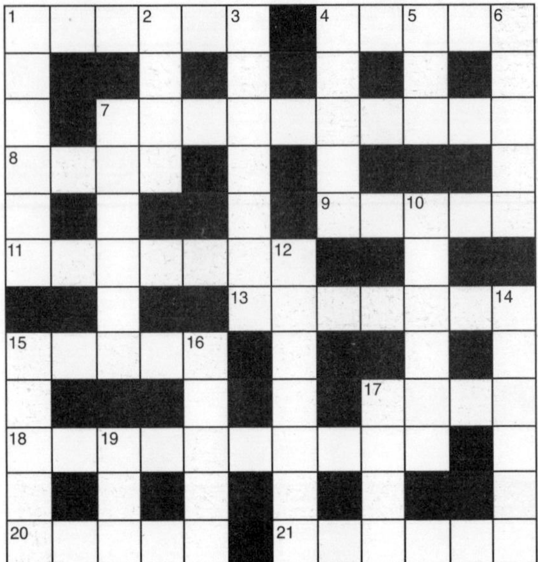

Across

1 Japanese dwarf tree (6)
4 Worth (5)
7 Dentures (5,5)
8 Conservative (4)
9 Defeated competitor (5)
11 Seek new members (7)
13 Hangs freely (7)
15 Foundation (5)
17 Assist (4)
18 Huge (10)
20 Exclusive news story (5)
21 Courteous (6)

Down

1 Straw hat (6)
2 Swing to and fro (4)
3 Lacking taste (7)
4 Essential (5)
5 Sheltered side (3)
6 Anaesthetic (5)
7 Noisy quarrel (6)
10 Abdominal organ (6)
12 Garment (4,3)
14 Having flexible joints (6)
15 Sham (5)
16 Rascal (5)
17 Vestibule (4)
19 Mr Ferdinand, footballer (3)

Across

1 Pretend (4,7)
7 Network (4)
8 Goes back on one's word (7)
9 Pen part (3)
10 Winter sportsman (5)
11 Fitting (6)
13 Boxing contests (6)
16 Work out (5)
18 Point a weapon (3)
19 Disregards (7)
20 Golf club (4)
21 Handsome (4-7)

Down

1 Kill (6)
2 Abduct (6)
3 Men's hairdresser (6)
4 Touches down (5)
5 Language (7)
6 Guarantees (7)
11 Transitory or momentary (7)
12 Florida city (7)
13 Humiliating failure (6)
14 Zodiac sign (6)
15 Crowd (6)
17 Enlist (5)

131

Across

1 Wash and iron (7)
7 Counting frame (6)
8 Room's upper surface (7)
9 Overdue (4)
10 Gibe (4)
12 Stifle (7)
14 Referee's item (7)
16 At the summit (4)
18 Spoken or verbal (4)
20 Dashing manner (7)
21 Light creamy dessert (6)
22 Revolves (7)

Down

1 Tetanus (7)
2 Unify (5)
3 Podium (4)
4 Style of jazz piano music (7)
5 Capital of Malta (8)
6 Reflected light (6)
11 Fidgety (8)
12 Light shoe (7)
13 Put down (7)
15 Extreme fear (6)
17 Unspoken (5)
19 Insect (4)

Across

1 Explain with pictures (10)
6 Rough drawing (6)
7 Stealing (5)
9 Funeral car (6)
10 Be indebted to (3)
11 Jelly type (4)
14 Shabby clothing (4)
15 Deity (3)
16 Tooth covering (6)
17 Fish (5)
18 Hairpiece (6)
20 Famous (10)

Down

1 Annoy (3)
2 Suds (6)
3 Globe (6)
4 Somewhat (6)
5 Abstaining from alcohol (8)
6 Direct (8)
8 Cherish (8)
9 Good-looking (8)
12 Mild (6)
13 Horse's gait (6)
14 Outcome (6)
19 Finish (3)

133

Across

1 Burial ground (9)
6 Affirmative (3)
8 Tarnishes (6)
9 Rub out (5)
10 Defraud or swindle (6)
11 Mr Chandler, writer (7)
13 Choices (7)
16 Sage (6)
18 Concerning (5)
19 Pandemonium (6)
21 Ovum (3)
22 Unkind or cruel (9)

Down

1 Acquire (3)
2 Tolerate (5)
3 Oriental (7)
4 Blood vessel (6)
5 Tirelessly active person (6)
7 Fast car (9)
8 Smother (9)
12 Assail (7)
14 Despite the fact that (6)
15 Canada's capital (6)
17 Edge (5)
20 Donkey (3)

Across

1 Competent (7)
5 Nobleman (4)
7 Vehicle (3)
8 Broadcast (8)
9 Hangman's halter (5)
10 Midday (4)
13 Roof slab (4)
14 Destroy (4)
18 Short letter (4)
19 Major artery (5)
21 World beater (8)
22 Destroy the insides of (3)
23 Soon (4)
24 Person selected (7)

Down

1 English city (8)
2 Scaly anteater (8)
3 Trouble (6)
4 ___ Paige, singer (6)
5 Tyrant (6)
6 Unite intimately (4)
11 Gaseous element (8)
12 Witty retort (8)
15 Mr Mailer, author (6)
16 Area (6)
17 Size of wine bottle (6)
20 Skinny (4)

135

Across

1 Woven cloth (6)
4 Money holder (5)
7 Unique (10)
8 Religious sisters (4)
9 Shoe fasteners (5)
11 Highland dress item (7)
13 Fielding position (4,3)
15 Board game (5)
17 Corrode (4)
18 Teacher (10)
20 Emblem (5)
21 Precious metal (6)

Down

1 Swoons (6)
2 Manages (4)
3 Causing laughter (7)
4 Flower part (5)
5 Chafe (3)
6 Gambling odds (5)
7 Revenue (6)
10 Red, say (6)
12 Beginners (7)
14 Assemble (6)
15 Ascend (5)
16 Rise in electric current (5)
17 Throw of dice (4)
19 Heavy-hearted (3)

Across

1 Cheap (11)
7 Box, in training (4)
8 Mr Crowe, actor (7)
9 Moisten (3)
10 Afterwards (5)
11 Stabbing weapon (6)
13 On fire (6)
16 Sudden fright (5)
18 So or thus (3)
19 Return to a former condition (7)
20 Osculate (4)
21 American state (11)

Down

1 Antelope (6)
2 Eavesdrop, informally (6)
3 Dark sweet ale (6)
4 Of the nose (5)
5 Inactivity (7)
6 Make bigger (7)
11 Drawing (7)
12 Spectacles (7)
13 Evaluate (6)
14 Imprison or confine (4,2)
15 Breakfast food (6)
17 Native New Zealander (5)

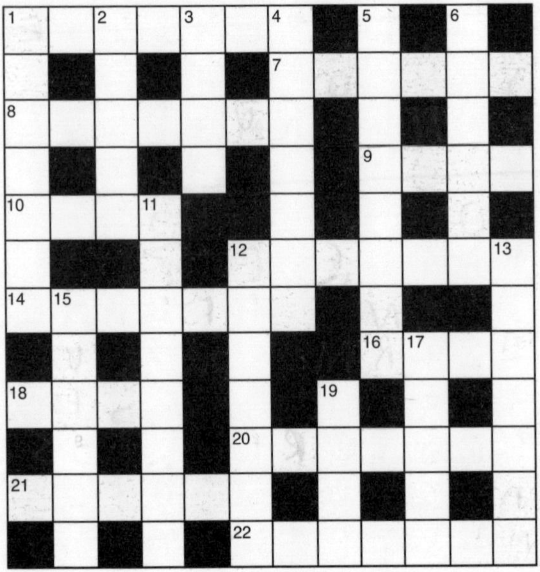

Across

1 Topmost (7)
7 Electronic messages (1-5)
8 Withstand (7)
9 Atmosphere (4)
10 Approximately (2,2)
12 Domed building (7)
14 Cooking room (7)
16 Discretion (4)
18 Therefore (4)
20 Radioactive element (7)
21 Permits (6)
22 Sincere (7)

Down

1 Kneeling cushion (7)
2 Sudden blasts of wind (5)
3 School test (4)
4 Stress (7)
5 Slingshot (8)
6 Glowered (6)
11 Opportunity (8)
12 Hermit (7)
13 Try (7)
15 Breathe in (6)
17 Living (5)
19 Couple (4)

Across

1 Decides or resolves (10)
6 Dazed state (6)
7 Indistinct (5)
9 Lavatory (6)
10 Born (3)
11 Unadulterated (4)
14 Bird's home (4)
15 Tavern (3)
16 Branched horn (6)
17 Antelope type (5)
18 Usual (6)
20 Intrusive (10)

Down

1 Speck (3)
2 Walk softly (6)
3 Hardly ever (6)
4 Ask along (6)
5 Mechanic (8)
6 Precious stone (8)
8 Ultimate (8)
9 Shorten by cutting (8)
12 Plain-spoken (6)
13 Batsman's posture (6)
14 Not far from (4,2)
19 Playing card (3)

Across

1 Quack (9)
6 Cigarette deposit (3)
8 Polite and respectable (6)
9 Start (5)
10 Christmas decoration (6)
11 Repeat (7)
13 Bureaucracy (3,4)
16 Rank or sour (6)
18 Additional (5)
19 Climb (6)
21 Golf peg (3)
22 Skilled storyteller (9)

Down

1 Actor's prompt (3)
2 Asserts (5)
3 Utter inadvertently (3,4)
4 Monarch's chair (6)
5 Queasiness (6)
7 Impetuous, excitable, etc. (3-6)
8 Cleansing agent (9)
12 Ground (7)
14 Be indecisive (6)
15 Foreign language (6)
17 Mother-of-pearl (5)
20 And not (3)

140

Across

1 Small hand axe (7)
5 Imitation (4)
7 Employ (3)
8 Ball game (8)
9 Light purple (5)
10 Regrets (4)
13 Italian capital (4)
14 Single photograph (4)
18 Flying toy (4)
19 Scope or extent (5)
21 Slaughter (8)
22 __ Wallach, actor (3)
23 Brogue, say (4)
24 Lengthen (7)

Down

1 Rude or surly (8)
2 Fail to notice (8)
3 Royal residence (6)
4 Happens again (6)
5 Maker of barrels (6)
6 Shove (4)
11 Hat type (8)
12 Young bird (8)
15 Paper handkerchief (6)
16 Drinking vessel (6)
17 Summerhouse (6)
20 Ready money (4)

141

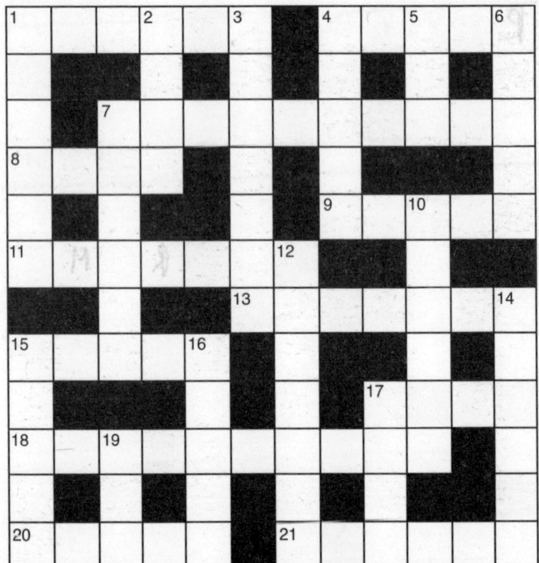

Across

1 Greek capital (6)
4 Backless shoes (5)
7 Awesomely impressive (10)
8 Epochs (4)
9 Lawful (5)
11 Learned person (7)
13 React (7)
15 Units of land (5)
17 Abominable snowman (4)
18 Unsweetened biscuit (4,6)
20 Perhaps (5)
21 Tray (6)

Down

1 Changes (6)
2 Cupid (4)
3 Meeting for discussion (7)
4 Mannequin (5)
5 Throw in a high arc (3)
6 Perfume (5)
7 Dad (6)
10 Stove (6)
12 Mends (7)
14 Motorist (6)
15 Stamp book (5)
16 Extent or range (5)
17 Scream (4)
19 Plaything (3)

Across

1 Assistance (7,4)
7 Hare's tail (4)
8 Quantities (7)
9 Label (3)
10 Baffling question (5)
11 Frightens (6)
13 Perspires (6)
16 Surpass (5)
18 Animal doctor (3)
19 Tread on and crush (7)
20 Unit of length (4)
21 Pitiless, relentless, etc. (11)

Down

1 Very busy and excited (6)
2 Untidy refuse (6)
3 Mental pictures (6)
4 Band (5)
5 Loss of memory (7)
6 Abandons (7)
11 Take refuge (7)
12 Approval (7)
13 Strict (6)
14 Complete (6)
15 Pamphlets (6)
17 Outcast (5)

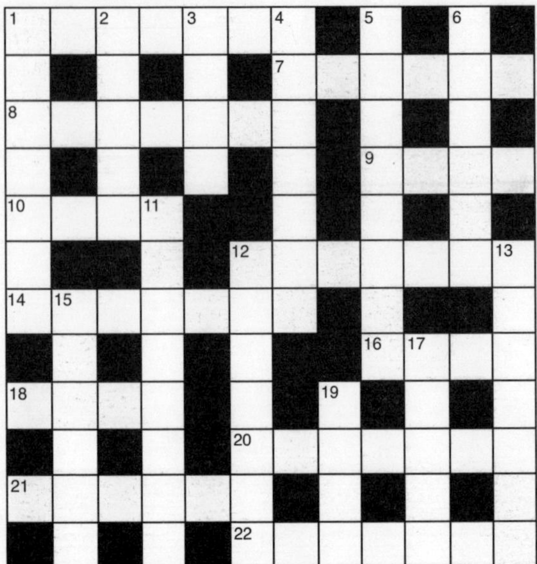

Across

1 Mixture or blend (7)
7 He flew too near the sun (6)
8 Small falcon (7)
9 Daring (4)
10 Yes votes (4)
12 Idea (7)
14 Ten-sided figure (7)
16 Paradise (4)
18 Edibles (4)
20 Teach (7)
21 Against (6)
22 Dealers or merchants (7)

Down

1 Difficult to manage (7)
2 Gangway (5)
3 Lass (4)
4 A thousand thousands (7)
5 Food cooked outside (8)
6 Filled to capacity (4,2)
11 Careless and hurried (8)
12 Competition (7)
13 Underground passages (7)
15 Wears away (6)
17 Hang in folds (5)
19 Cougar (4)

Across

1 Amity (10)
6 Belief (6)
7 Log boats (5)
9 Happening not long ago (6)
10 A low (3)
11 Require (4)
14 Is obliged to (4)
15 Enemy (3)
16 Editions (6)
17 Raising agent (5)
18 Amongst (6)
20 Molotov cocktail (6,4)

Down

1 In favour of (3)
2 Certainly (6)
3 Aromatic spice (6)
4 Elfin creature (6)
5 Notorious (8)
6 Daddy-longlegs (5,3)
8 Quicker route (5,3)
9 Traitor (8)
12 Cold season (6)
13 Assault (6)
14 Country (6)
19 Weep (3)

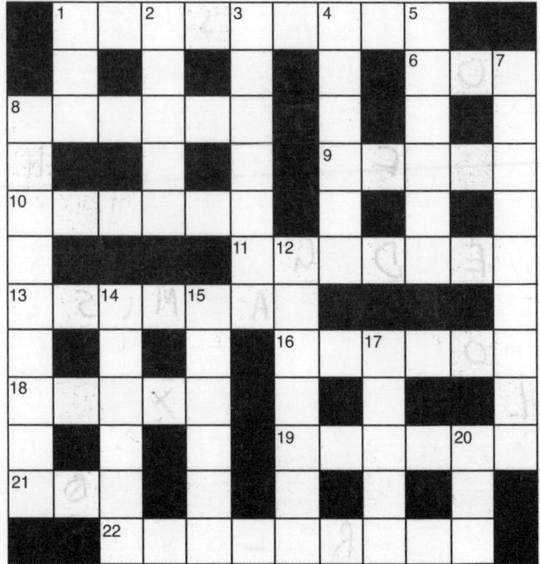

Across

1 Gear (9)
6 Sing with closed lips (3)
8 Sikh's headdress (6)
9 Alliance (5)
10 Picturesque (6)
11 Level of command (7)
13 Inorganic matter (7)
16 Soak up (6)
18 Domesticates (5)
19 Move about hurriedly (6)
21 Shade of colour (3)
22 Unwilling (9)

Down

1 Australian bird (3)
2 Of a town (5)
3 Universal remedy (7)
4 Sufficient (6)
5 Exciting feeling (6)
7 From childhood (3,3,3)
8 Cricket international (4,5)
12 Vintage (7)
14 Add up to (6)
15 Scamp (6)
17 Steam bath (5)
20 Rodent (3)

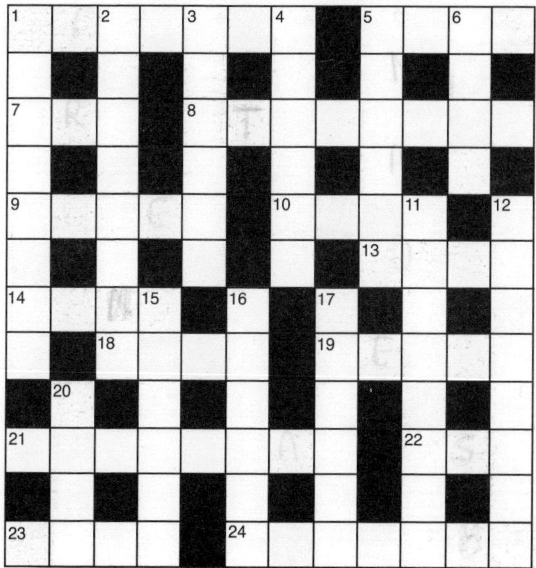

Across

1 Exact copy (7)
5 Strongbox (4)
7 Male offspring (3)
8 Private feud (8)
9 Intends (5)
10 Three feet (4)
13 Painful (4)
14 Housetop (4)
18 African river (4)
19 Takes notice of (5)
21 Headway (8)
22 Hill (3)
23 Undiluted (4)
24 Chooses (7)

Down

1 Culinary herb (8)
2 Five-sided figure (8)
3 Put money in (6)
4 Riles (6)
5 Guides (6)
6 Destiny (4)
11 Of the home or family (8)
12 Reprimands (8)
15 Move about restlessly (6)
16 Gems (6)
17 Hand tool (6)
20 Costing nothing (4)

147

Across

1 Cause to remember (6)
4 Skinflint (5)
7 Pious (3-7)
8 Gemstone (4)
9 Cold dish (5)
11 Monotonous (7)
13 Diminish (7)
15 Conditions (5)
17 Quick or furtive look (4)
18 Gum tree (10)
20 A hold-up (5)
21 Straightforward (6)

Down

1 Rebellion (6)
2 Object of worship (4)
3 Swindle (7)
4 Grumbles or complains (5)
5 Snow runner (3)
6 Stiff (5)
7 Male goose (6)
10 Women (6)
12 Deluged (7)
14 Send goods abroad (6)
15 Tyre surface (5)
16 Saline (5)
17 Cat noise (4)
19 Mountain pass (3)

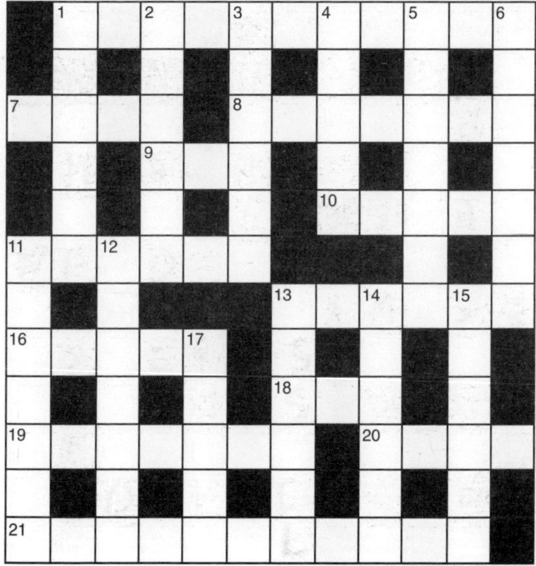

Across

1 Star sign (11)
7 Cooked animal flesh (4)
8 Draw towards (7)
9 Chew and swallow (3)
10 Casino counters (5)
11 Exactly that (2,4)
13 Guarantee (6)
16 Imitate (5)
18 Curve (3)
19 Spite (7)
20 Slay (4)
21 Very brave (4-7)

Down

1 Large scissors (6)
2 Rich cake (6)
3 Roofing material (6)
4 Garret (5)
5 Picture mentally (7)
6 Sate (7)
11 Naval commander (7)
12 Souvenir (7)
13 Ancient Greek city (6)
14 Type of firework (6)
15 Laboured (6)
17 Woven fabric (5)

149

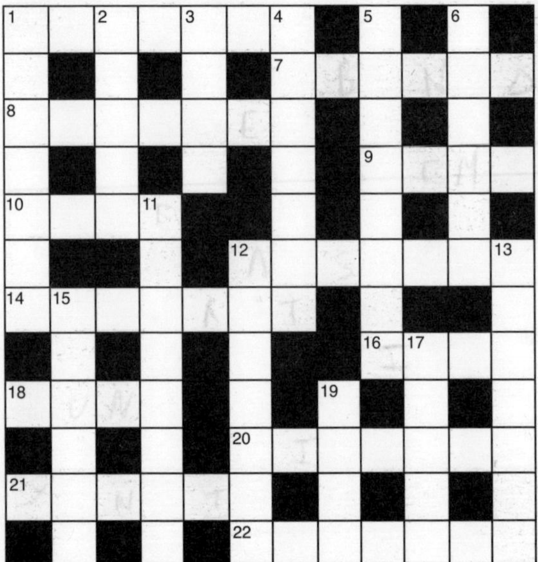

Across

1 Piece of furniture (7)
7 Alleviation (6)
8 Excite or trouble (7)
9 Ballet skirt (4)
10 Whip (4)
12 Dives (7)
14 Import illegally (7)
16 Bill of fare (4)
18 Increase in size (4)
20 Medium (7)
21 Looking glass (6)
22 Afters (7)

Down

1 Mr Kennedy, MP (7)
2 Perfect happiness (5)
3 Close to (4)
4 Quiver (7)
5 Precious metal (8)
6 Middle point (6)
11 Tightrope (4,4)
12 Poster (7)
13 Pupil (7)
15 Spearfish (6)
17 Elude (5)
19 Untidy state (4)

Across

1 Intentional (10)
6 Couch (6)
7 Multiplied by (5)
9 Glib rapid speech (6)
10 Rowing blade (3)
11 Beak (4)
14 Labyrinth (4)
15 __ Gardner, actress (3)
16 Yearly (6)
17 Intoxicated (5)
18 Untouched or unimpaired (6)
20 Bolsters (10)

Down

1 Owing (3)
2 Deadly (6)
3 Baas (6)
4 Go back (6)
5 Relating to time (8)
6 Sword holder (8)
8 Noncommissioned officer (8)
9 Enjoyment, satisfaction, etc. (8)
12 Serviette (6)
13 Spectral colour (6)
14 Putty-like substance (6)
19 Lettuce (3)

151

Across

1 Act of spying (9)
6 Signal agreement (3)
8 Reason (6)
9 Appears (5)
10 Revoke (6)
11 Helps (7)
13 Extract (7)
16 To or from each one (6)
18 Female relatives (5)
19 Foolish people (6)
21 Monetary unit (3)
22 Swapped (9)

Down

1 The self (3)
2 Group of lions (5)
3 Cover and extend beyond (7)
4 Maltreats (6)
5 Goes in (6)
7 Calamities (9)
8 Soldier of fortune (9)
12 Staying power (7)
14 Doglike (6)
15 Rural (6)
17 Cake decoration (5)
20 Mr Danson, actor (3)

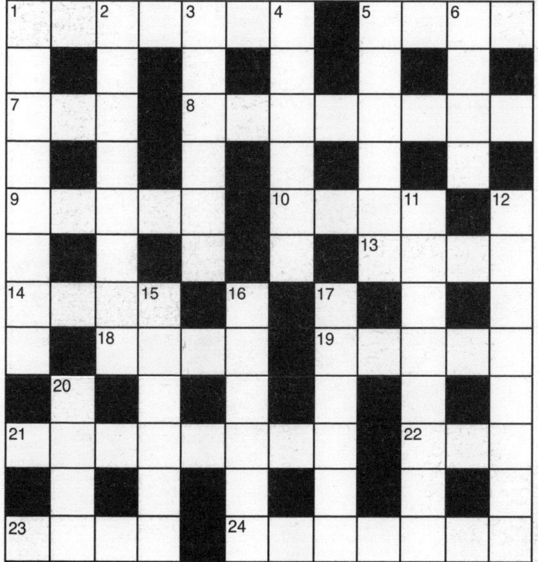

152

Across

1 Area of fruit trees (7)
5 Coarse file (4)
7 Hawaiian garland (3)
8 Salad dish (8)
9 Happen (5)
10 Sepulchre (4)
13 Therefore (4)
14 Public school (4)
18 Badly off (4)
19 Speed contests (5)
21 Dainty (8)
22 Lyric poem (3)
23 Knock senseless (4)
24 Foes (7)

Down

1 Spectator (8)
2 Sound of a horse walking (4-4)
3 Agreement (6)
4 Expunge (6)
5 Begin again (6)
6 Close angrily (4)
11 Vegetable (8)
12 Supports or reinforces (8)
15 Idea (6)
16 Invent (6)
17 Gentle wind (6)
20 Immediately following (4)

153

Across

1 Prairie wolf (6)
4 Sham (5)
7 Mercy killing (10)
8 Fathers (4)
9 Swagger (5)
11 Stretchy (7)
13 Boast (4,3)
15 Bravery award (5)
17 City in Nevada (4)
18 Very precise about details (10)
20 Odour (5)
21 Gives in (6)

Down

1 Wax stick (6)
2 Burden (4)
3 Display (7)
4 Marriage proclamation (5)
5 Household fuel (3)
6 Well-kept (5)
7 Mr Fox, actor (6)
10 Gemstones (6)
12 Horse soldiers (7)
14 Spheres (6)
15 Contagious viral disease (5)
16 Provincial (5)
17 Stratagem (4)
19 Drawn match (3)

154

Across

1 In vogue (11)
7 Spoken or verbal (4)
8 Unusually large (7)
9 Fuss (3)
10 Use a razor (5)
11 Clever, informally (6)
13 Anticipate (6)
16 Following in time (5)
18 Unwell (3)
19 Woman's item (7)
20 Greek letter (4)
21 Male relative (11)

Down

1 Erstwhile (6)
2 Highly-spiced sausage (6)
3 Foolishness (6)
4 Titles (5)
5 Swathe (7)
6 Component (7)
11 Wrestling hold (4,3)
12 Feeler (7)
13 Mystery (6)
14 Buff (6)
15 Horse's gait (6)
17 Zealous (5)

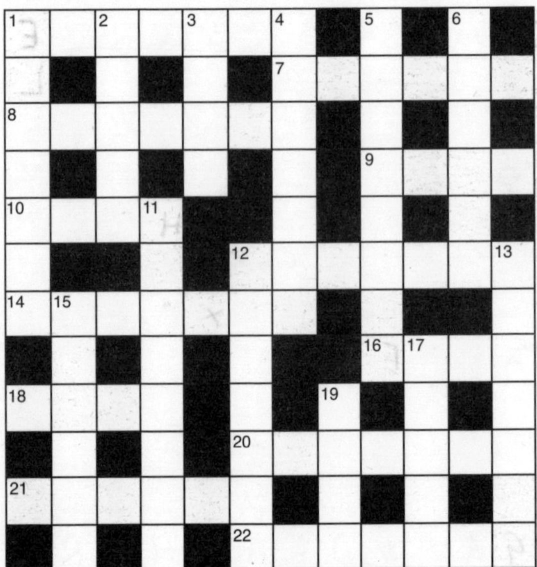

155

Across

1 Minor deity (7)
7 Breathe out (6)
8 Jails (7)
9 Cooking fat (4)
10 Prophet (4)
12 Large ape (7)
14 Weekday (7)
16 Stop (4)
18 Locate (4)
20 Place apart (7)
21 Tim Henman's sport (6)
22 Occurs (7)

Down

1 Down payment (7)
2 American state (5)
3 Virtuous (4)
4 Ruin (7)
5 Silly, immature, etc. (8)
6 Of flowers (6)
11 Junior doctor (8)
12 To decorate (7)
13 Female thespian (7)
15 Joined (6)
17 Astonish (5)
19 Broth (4)

Across

- **1** Free enterprise (10)
- **6** Drive or push forward (6)
- **7** Move to music (5)
- **9** Spiritualists' meeting (6)
- **10** Towboat (3)
- **11** Fossil fuel (4)
- **14** The two (4)
- **15** Zodiac sign (3)
- **16** Catchword (6)
- **17** Topic (5)
- **18** Temperament (6)
- **20** Thin dry biscuit (10)

Down

- **1** Vehicle (3)
- **2** Marionette (6)
- **3** Claws (6)
- **4** Stocking run (6)
- **5** Authorisation (8)
- **6** Booklet (8)
- **8** Albumen (3,5)
- **9** Destroyer (8)
- **12** Valuable things (6)
- **13** Socialise informally (6)
- **14** Combat (6)
- **19** Stick or shaft (3)

157

Across

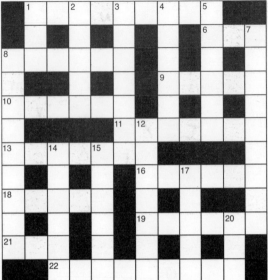

1 Goal or aim (9)
6 Fish (3)
8 Engineless aircraft (6)
9 Articles (5)
10 Faithful, reliable, etc. (6)
11 Function (7)
13 Join together (7)
16 Eye membrane (6)
18 Illegal burning (5)
19 Dilate (6)
21 Gardening tool (3)
22 Unbelieving (9)

Down

1 Lubricant (3)
2 Traitor (5)
3 Continue or persevere (5,2)
4 Within (6)
5 Skin condition (6)
7 Ignore (9)
8 Enter uninvited (4-5)
12 Ideal (7)
14 Fails to hit (6)
15 Congenital (6)
17 Theme (5)
20 Nothing (3)

Across

1 Colour (7)
5 Indian dress (4)
7 Meadow (3)
8 Contorts the face (8)
9 Military trainee (5)
10 Space (4)
13 Broad (4)
14 Plunder (4)
18 Never a one (4)
19 Abrupt (5)
21 Permission to proceed (3,5)
22 Water when frozen (3)
23 Soon (4)
24 Cleaning cloths (7)

Down

1 Very small particle (8)
2 Male relative (8)
3 Nullify (6)
4 Place where bees are kept (6)
5 Follow secretly (6)
6 Spool (4)
11 Sick headache (8)
12 Football officials (8)
15 Tropical American bird (6)
16 Protect (6)
17 Begins (6)
20 Tribe (4)

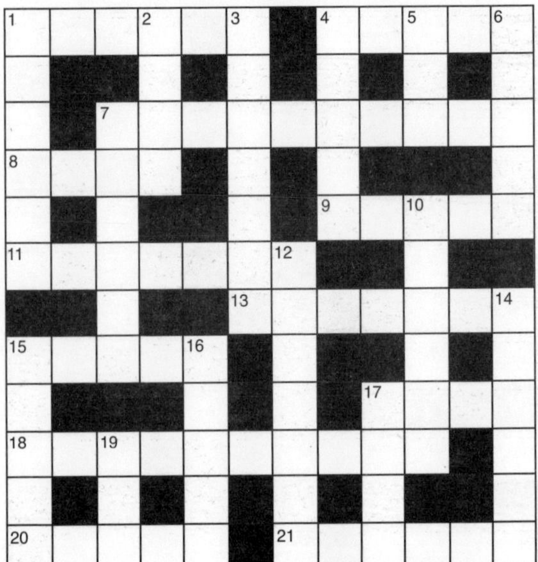

Across

1 Subsides (6)
4 Taut (5)
7 Bad luck (10)
8 Cheese type (4)
9 Sailing vessel (5)
11 A town in Wiltshire (7)
13 Not artificial (7)
15 Fashion (5)
17 Chimney deposit (4)
18 Skilled (10)
20 Stupid pupil (5)
21 Give in (6)

Down

1 Vipers (6)
2 Light haircut (4)
3 Crocus (7)
4 To delay (5)
5 Wildebeest (3)
6 Delightful surprise (5)
7 Of the sea (6)
10 Vegetable (6)
12 Diapers (7)
14 Most recent (6)
15 Lukewarm (5)
16 Ambition (5)
17 Insult deliberately (4)
19 Possess (3)

Across

1 Outgoings (11)
7 Cut or knock down (4)
8 Conspicuous (7)
9 Soft fruit (3)
10 Bobbin (5)
11 Rue (6)
13 Mischievous jokes (6)
16 Sudden fear (5)
18 Fish eggs (3)
19 Piercing screams (7)
20 Unfeeling (4)
21 Blown-up photo (11)

Down

1 Come into view (6)
2 Filch (6)
3 Lump of gold (6)
4 Mosque prayer leaders (5)
5 Mythical creature (7)
6 Swallows up (7)
11 Sharp reply (7)
12 Common (7)
13 Run after (6)
14 A broad street (6)
15 Fate or destiny (6)
17 Free of obstruction (5)

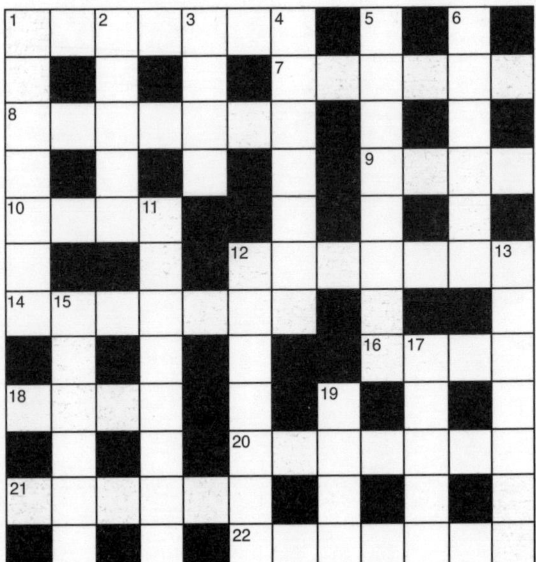

161

Across

1 Sheltered port (7)
7 Finger-shaped cake (6)
8 Minor illness (7)
9 Waterfowl (4)
10 Group of cattle (4)
12 Panacea (4-3)
14 Remarkable or distinguished (7)
16 Midday (4)
18 Hitlerite (4)
20 Difficult to catch (7)
21 Purchased (6)
22 Insults (7)

Down

1 Pagan (7)
2 Measuring stick (5)
3 Unlock (4)
4 Entourage (7)
5 Cosh (8)
6 Of public revenue (6)
11 Business relations (8)
12 Near (5,2)
13 Delays or loiters (7)
15 Public speaker (6)
17 Edible bulb (5)
19 Large deep bay (4)

Across

1 Prying person, informally (4,6)
6 Hidden gunman (6)
7 Hard part of bread (5)
9 Unit of time (6)
10 Limb (3)
11 Entrance (4)
14 Fruit (4)
15 Aged (3)
16 Wan (6)
17 Root vegetable (5)
18 Lacking width (6)
20 Evaluation (10)

Down

1 Religious sister (3)
2 Late meal (6)
3 Absolve (6)
4 Ebb (6)
5 Tried to be like (8)
6 Given to study (8)
8 The day after today (8)
9 Troops (8)
12 Globe (6)
13 Window shades (6)
14 Mr Brosnan, actor (6)
19 Choose (3)

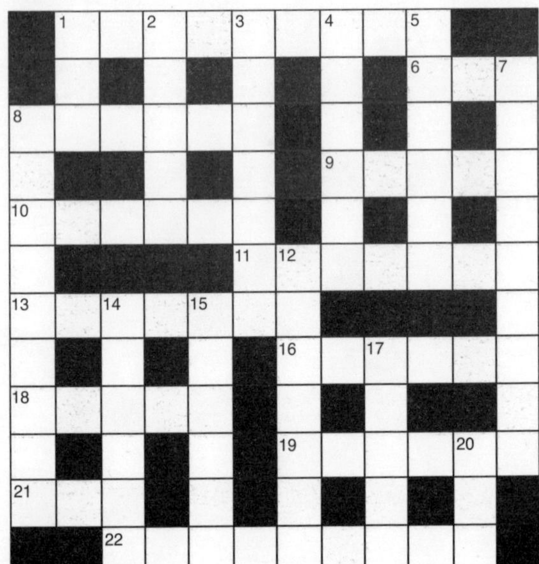

Across

1 Mafia boss (9)
6 Ventilate (3)
8 Needle (6)
9 Flowers (5)
10 Falling star (6)
11 Everlasting (7)
13 Bewilder (7)
16 Treble (6)
18 Boors (5)
19 Naturist (6)
21 Born as (3)
22 Aide (9)

Down

1 Acquire (3)
2 Search deeply (5)
3 Convinces (7)
4 Funeral car (6)
5 Dried grape (6)
7 Elastic (9)
8 Punctuation mark (9)
12 Lockjaw (7)
14 Feeling of revulsion (6)
15 Tips over (6)
17 Country (5)
20 Chronic drunkard (3)

Across

1 Eight-sided figure (7)
5 Thick paper (4)
7 Pitch (3)
8 Word for word (8)
9 Smell (5)
10 First man (4)
13 Commotion or fuss (2-2)
14 As well (4)
18 Gaelic (4)
19 Stealing (5)
21 Estrange (8)
22 Girl's name (3)
23 Vend (4)
24 Infinite (7)

Down

1 Left to personal choice (8)
2 Slow-moving creature (8)
3 Rule (6)
4 Usual (6)
5 Neckwear item (6)
6 Wet weather (4)
11 Middle-of-the-road (8)
12 Ingredients (8)
15 Difficult experience (6)
16 Ten years (6)
17 Be present at (6)
20 Run away (4)

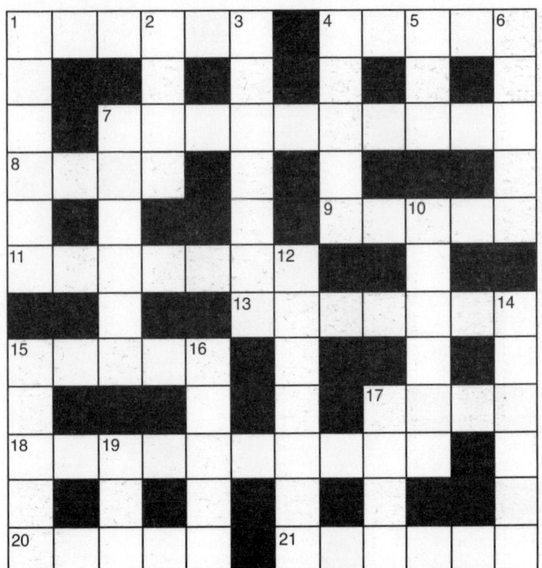

Across

1 Comment (6)
4 Raises (5)
7 Plastic bullet (5,5)
8 At any time (4)
9 Croons (5)
11 Farm vehicle (7)
13 Roams (7)
15 Sugary (5)
17 Nuisance (4)
18 American city (3,7)
20 Period of darkness (5)
21 Fish (6)

Down

1 Begrudge (6)
2 Slightly open (4)
3 Ingenuity, skill, etc. (4-3)
4 Noblemen (5)
5 Viral infection, in short (3)
6 Flanks (5)
7 Scold harshly (6)
10 Female relatives (6)
12 Bacon slices (7)
14 Planet (6)
15 Hairdresser's shop (5)
16 Belief (5)
17 Ringing of bells (4)
19 Hang heavily (3)

Across

1 Matador, say (11)
7 Search systematically (4)
8 Ineffectual (7)
9 Ovum (3)
10 Private teacher (5)
11 Container for liquid (6)
13 Dairy product (6)
16 Roofing slabs (5)
18 Belonging to us (3)
19 Motives (7)
20 Press clothes (4)
21 Primitive (11)

Down

1 Yellowish-brown colour (6)
2 Tags (6)
3 Thrifty (6)
4 Big (5)
5 Operating room (7)
6 Keep for oneself (7)
11 Old soldier (7)
12 Seedless raisin (7)
13 Nearer (6)
14 Increase the wealth of (6)
15 Saunter (6)
17 Scimitar, say (5)

167

Across

1 Charm and allure (7)
7 Follows (6)
8 Idlers (7)
9 Otherwise (4)
10 Skin problem (4)
12 Cheerful and optimistic (7)
14 Prickly plant (7)
16 Settee (4)
18 Information (4)
20 Golf clubs (7)
21 Determine (6)
22 A hold-up (7)

Down

1 Chivalrous (7)
2 Once more (5)
3 Bulls, cows, etc. (4)
4 Remainder (7)
5 In addition to (2,4,2)
6 Population count (6)
11 Rapturous (8)
12 Liquidiser (7)
13 Gossip (7)
15 Paradise (6)
17 Excessively fat (5)
19 Arm or leg (4)

Across

1 Clavicle (10)
6 Of the mind (6)
7 Wanderer (5)
9 Type of music (6)
10 Facial twitch (3)
11 Extended journey (4)
14 Tolerate or endure (4)
15 __ MacGraw, actress (3)
16 Pantry (6)
17 Rub out (5)
18 Invent or contrive (6)
20 Percussion instrument (10)

Down

1 Snooker rod (3)
2 Missive (6)
3 State without proof (6)
4 Golf hazard (6)
5 Regardless of (2,6)
6 Home loan agreement (8)
8 Adorn (8)
9 Meditate or ponder (8)
12 Even though (6)
13 River crossing (6)
14 Amphibious rodent (6)
19 Total (3)

Across

1 After childbirth (9)
6 On strike (3)
8 Next to (6)
9 Muscle pain (5)
10 Stoat-like mammal (6)
11 Oriental (7)
13 Storm (7)
16 Deposit on teeth (6)
18 Swiftness (5)
19 High-kicking dance (6)
21 Knight's title (3)
22 Plimsolls (9)

Down

1 Baked food (3)
2 Rotates (5)
3 Knitting rods (7)
4 Vestiges (6)
5 Find (6)
7 Form of cricket (3,3,3)
8 Casts a spell over (9)
12 Sets upon (7)
14 Skinflints (6)
15 Number (6)
17 Mr Starr, drummer (5)
20 Donkey (3)

Across

1 Poison (7)
5 Joke (4)
7 Knock (3)
8 Photo developing place (8)
9 Manservant (5)
10 Cease (4)
13 Short letter (4)
14 Status (4)
18 Story (4)
19 Group of eight (5)
21 Long race (8)
22 Weapon (3)
23 Eyelid inflammation (4)
24 Determination (7)

Down

1 Ant bear (8)
2 Take the place of (8)
3 Nakedness (6)
4 Stroke gently (6)
5 Technical language (6)
6 Shortly (4)
11 Country (8)
12 Impose imprisonment on (8)
15 Martial art (6)
16 Tie up (6)
17 Adds up (6)
20 Condiment (4)

171

Across

1 Large prawns (6)
4 Very bad (5)
7 Lucrative (10)
8 Seven days (4)
9 Goes by horse (5)
11 Archbishop (7)
13 Allow (7)
15 Anaesthetic (5)
17 Musical instrument (4)
18 Sleeveless garment (4,6)
20 Sport (5)
21 High-pitched and piercing (6)

Down

1 Embarrass (4,2)
2 Grade work (4)
3 Blow air into (7)
4 Jude Law, say (5)
5 Petty lie (3)
6 English city (5)
7 Die (6)
10 Roundabout route (6)
12 Guarantees (7)
14 Tooth covering (6)
15 Cinder (5)
16 Loud and disorderly (5)
17 Rip (4)
19 Use a spade (3)

Across

1 Peace offering (5,6)
7 Complete extent (4)
8 Expresses admiration for (7)
9 Be indebted to (3)
10 Work out (5)
11 Hate (6)
13 Elegant (6)
16 Outstanding (5)
18 Mr Stewart, singer (3)
19 Comprise (7)
20 Nobleman (4)
21 Treacle (6,5)

Down

1 Be against (6)
2 Take no notice of (6)
3 Specialist (6)
4 Bellows (5)
5 Snuggles (7)
6 Socks, stockings, etc. (7)
11 Spirited (7)
12 Of current affairs (7)
13 Coercion (6)
14 Make beloved (6)
15 Incite (4,2)
17 Chosen way (5)

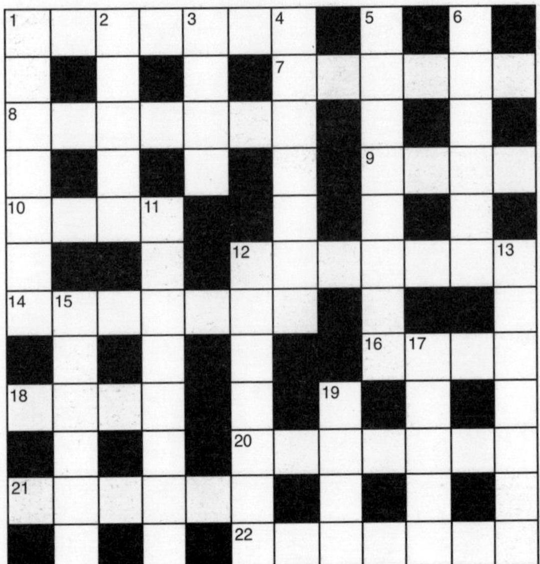

Across

1 Mounted bullfighter (7)
7 Perfect society (6)
8 Uproar (7)
9 Meat spread (4)
10 Sully (4)
12 Gift (7)
14 Reveal or expose (3,4)
16 Bring up (4)
18 __ Thompson, actress (4)
20 Obstinate or stupid (7)
21 Expandable bullet (6)
22 Sincere (7)

Down

1 Sunshade (7)
2 Prickly plants (5)
3 Fall in drops (4)
4 English town (7)
5 Music writer (8)
6 Lend an ear (6)
11 Panthers (8)
12 Nom de plume (3,4)
13 Torture (7)
15 Protective clothing (6)
17 Exclusive (5)
19 Jetty (4)

Across

1 Snapshot (10)
6 Card suit (6)
7 Hand digit (5)
9 Nab (6)
10 A female sheep (3)
11 Policemen, slang (4)
14 Wound mark (4)
15 Number (3)
16 Hot beverage (6)
17 Soft wet earth (5)
18 Very young child (6)
20 Patron (10)

Down

1 Short explosive sound (3)
2 Commands (6)
3 Shellfish (6)
4 Revolve or spin (6)
5 Caution in practical affairs (8)
6 Roomy (8)
8 Salad vegetable (8)
9 Desire for food (8)
12 Secret plot (6)
13 Continent (6)
14 Consider proper (3,3)
19 And not (3)

175

Across

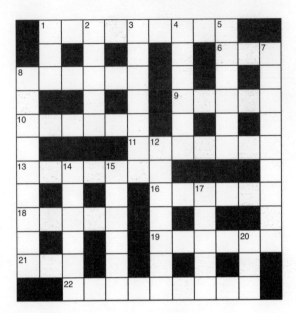

1 Active at night (9)
6 Small bristle on barley (3)
8 Diffuse (6)
9 Bury (5)
10 Cavort (6)
11 Spire (7)
13 Revive or reinvigorate (7)
16 To drink (6)
18 Two times (5)
19 Employers (6)
21 Regret (3)
22 Frantic (9)

Down

1 Pinch (3)
2 Free from dirt (5)
3 Remove one's clothes (7)
4 Beginner (6)
5 Portable computer (6)
7 Calm and collected (9)
8 Very famous celebrity (9)
12 Sewing aid (7)
14 Thwarted (6)
15 Happenings (6)
17 Iraqi port (5)
20 Viewing organ (3)

Across

1 Aquatic bird (7)
5 Of low temperature (4)
7 Tavern (3)
8 Regain possession of (8)
9 Requires (5)
10 Conceited (4)
13 Traffic marker (4)
14 Unguis (4)
18 Compass point (4)
19 In that place (5)
21 Client (8)
22 Anger (3)
23 Dread (4)
24 Soon (7)

Down

1 Painful to the feelings (8)
2 Women's underwear (8)
3 Colour (6)
4 Indigenous (6)
5 Medical centre (6)
6 Be very fond of (4)
11 Author (8)
12 Burial ground (8)
15 Second of two (6)
16 Postage labels (6)
17 Hi-fi (6)
20 Gargantuan (4)

177

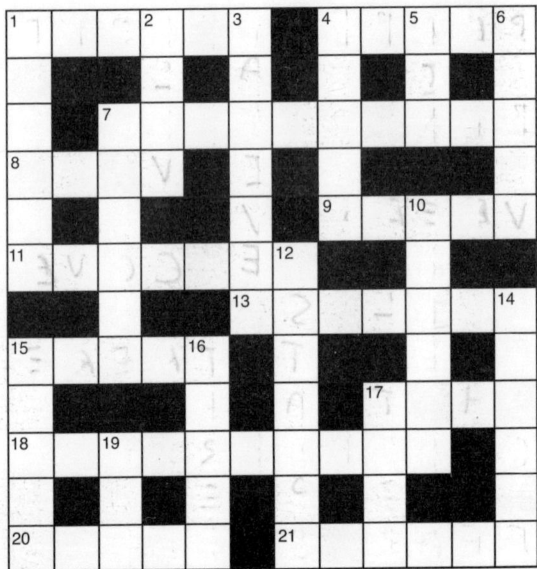

Across

1 Soldier who digs trenches (6)
4 Pulsate (5)
7 One's finest clothes (6,4)
8 Streetcar (4)
9 Planet (5)
11 Imitator (7)
13 Bewails (7)
15 Lustre (5)
17 Fever (4)
18 Capsize (4,6)
20 American cattle farm (5)
21 Irritates (6)

Down

1 Stationary (6)
2 Fruit (4)
3 Fundamental (7)
4 Aromatic herb (5)
5 Fish eggs (3)
6 Female dog (5)
7 Specimen (6)
10 Go back on one's word (6)
12 Greek restaurant (7)
14 Perspires (6)
15 Indian instrument (5)
16 Nick (5)
17 Football's Mr Shearer (4)
19 Manage (3)

Across

1 Rodent type (3,8)
7 Ballet skirt (4)
8 Refrain from voting (7)
9 Drinks counter (3)
10 Levy (5)
11 Plant with edible stalks (6)
13 Mass departure (6)
16 Practice exams (5)
18 Illuminated (3)
19 Loss of memory (7)
20 Small and weakly (4)
21 Slows down (11)

Down

1 Russian monetary unit (6)
2 Twice as much (6)
3 Prey (6)
4 Picture within another (5)
5 Responded (7)
6 Surgical knives (7)
11 Order (7)
12 Terse (7)
13 Cream cake (6)
14 Production (6)
15 Planet (6)
17 Rope-making fibre (5)

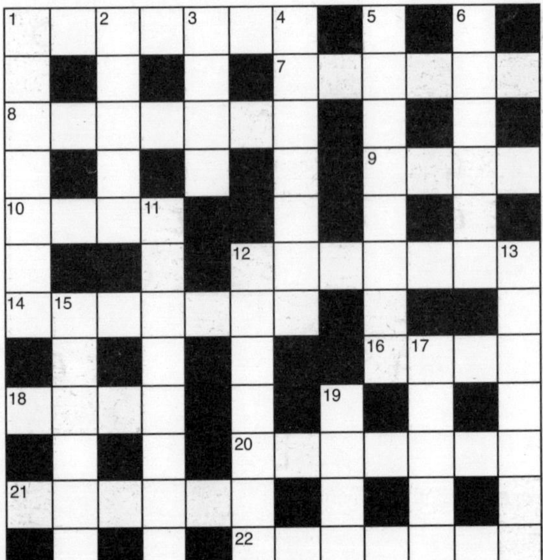

Across

1 Eye make-up (7)
7 Tall grass-like plant (6)
8 Hot condiment (7)
9 Pakistani language (4)
10 Pig noise (4)
12 Adhesive label (7)
14 Repulsive (7)
16 Store (4)
18 Bereavement (4)
20 Etch (7)
21 Equipment (6)
22 Scoffs at (7)

Down

1 Colossal (7)
2 Girl's name (5)
3 Way off (4)
4 Kidnaps (7)
5 Thrashes (8)
6 Interfere (6)
11 Memento (8)
12 Achieve one's aim (7)
13 Put down (7)
15 Line on a weather map (6)
17 Hidden store (5)
19 Jelly type (4)

Across

1 One who talks a lot (10)
6 Container for liquids (6)
7 Meat in rashers (5)
9 As well (2,4)
10 Weaken (3)
11 Car's hooter (4)
14 Crossbow missile (4)
15 Possess (3)
16 Fixed allowance (6)
17 American city (5)
18 Preserve after death (6)
20 Resolute (10)

Down

1 Dove's call (3)
2 Deed (6)
3 Minor earthquake (6)
4 Automata (6)
5 Opportunity (8)
6 Lavatory, euphemistically (8)
8 Favouritism towards relatives (8)
9 Cut short (8)
12 Contusion (6)
13 Small river (6)
14 Spool (6)
19 Boy (3)

Across

1 Mouth organ (9)
6 Hill (3)
8 Mark of disgrace (6)
9 Fit out (5)
10 Small restaurant (6)
11 Paying guests (7)
13 Revokes (7)
16 Corsair (6)
18 Light boat (5)
19 Bursts out (6)
21 Prosecute (3)
22 Of short duration (9)

Down

1 Trilby, say (3)
2 Correct (5)
3 Enjoying continued success (2,1,4)
4 Certainly (6)
5 Adjust or accustom (6)
7 Take back (9)
8 Deducts (9)
12 Fish-eating birds (7)
14 Small basket for fruit (6)
15 Schedule (6)
17 Red cosmetic (5)
20 Toddler (3)

Across

1 Seem probable (3,4)
5 Immense (4)
7 Point a weapon (3)
8 Revealed (8)
9 Smithy (5)
10 Ruminant mammal (4)
13 Mechanical routine (4)
14 Uncommon (4)
18 Land measure (4)
19 Hangman's halter (5)
21 Winsome (8)
22 Obtained (3)
23 This place (4)
24 Beginner (7)

Down

1 English city (8)
2 Brown sugar (8)
3 ___ Hepburn, actress (6)
4 Plunder (6)
5 Crude (6)
6 Plant ovule (4)
11 Sleigh (8)
12 Soldier who runs away (8)
15 Card game (6)
16 Servile (6)
17 Mystery (6)
20 Brogue, say (4)

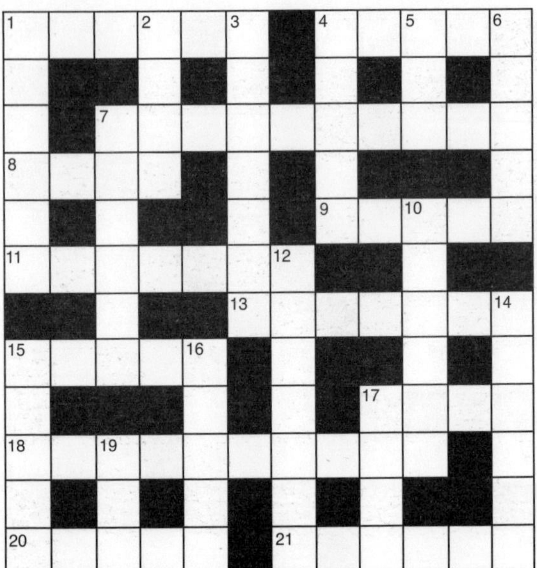

Across

1 Handgun (6)
4 Stop (5)
7 Bird type (10)
8 Boy's name (4)
9 Holy book (5)
11 Middle (7)
13 Dictionary (7)
15 Greek letter (5)
17 Immediately following (4)
18 Tennis term (3-7)
20 Bishop's headdress (5)
21 Delay or hold back (6)

Down

1 Meal from a hamper (6)
2 End part (4)
3 According to reason (7)
4 Ascend (5)
5 Cigarette deposit (3)
6 Weird (5)
7 Doghouse (6)
10 Squabble (6)
12 Gymnast's outfit (7)
14 Idea (6)
15 Fact (5)
16 Concur (5)
17 Shipshape (4)
19 Consume (3)

Across

1 Mercury (11)
7 New Zealand bird (4)
8 Greek letter (7)
9 Policeman, slang (3)
10 Electronic message (1-4)
11 Boy's name (6)
13 Roof tiles (6)
16 Theme (5)
18 Recede (3)
19 Rude, insulting, etc. (7)
20 Resound (4)
21 One influencing fashion (11)

Down

1 Tremble (6)
2 Frozen spike (6)
3 Persist in (4,2)
4 Edition (5)
5 Brave (7)
6 Festers (7)
11 Pull out (7)
12 Outer planet (7)
13 Shirt part (6)
14 Watch chain (6)
15 One or the other (6)
17 Young human (5)

185

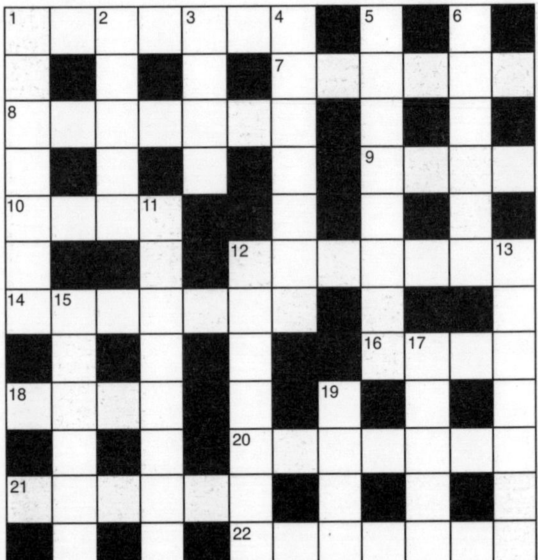

Across

1 Vegetable type (7)
7 Person in charge (6)
8 Bird's feathers (7)
9 Pavement edge (4)
10 Chooses (4)
12 Photographer, informally (7)
14 Dubious (7)
16 Ridge of coral (4)
18 Fibber (4)
20 White ant (7)
21 Mild (6)
22 Rues (7)

Down

1 Abundant (7)
2 Lacking sharpness (5)
3 Saracen (4)
4 Refined, chic, etc. (7)
5 Delphinium (8)
6 Boy's name (6)
11 To part (8)
12 Child's vehicle (7)
13 Roof beams (7)
15 Unified (6)
17 Banishment (5)
19 Talk big (4)

Across

1 Fluffy confection (10)
6 Descent by rope (6)
7 Eerie (5)
9 Decipher (6)
10 Woman's long scarf (3)
11 Plant type (4)
14 Wintry weather (4)
15 Insect (3)
16 Work up (6)
17 Afterwards (5)
18 Disburse (6)
20 Instrument of torture (4,6)

Down

1 Young fox (3)
2 Female relatives (6)
3 Colour (6)
4 Solicitor, for example (6)
5 Tibia (8)
6 Everything considered (3,2,3)
8 Useless person, informally (8)
9 Tyrannical ruler (8)
12 Iran's capital (6)
13 Skin condition (6)
14 Daft (6)
19 Religious sister (3)

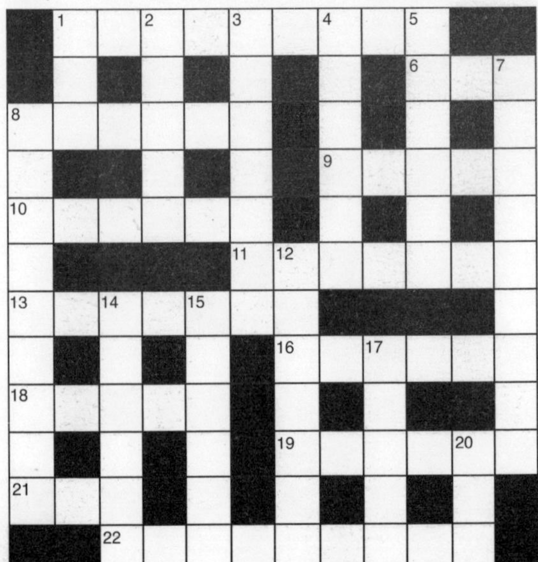

Across

1 Squeeze-box (9)
6 Aged (3)
8 Drawing implement (6)
9 Valuable thing (5)
10 Antelope (6)
11 Cowboy hat (7)
13 Authorise (7)
16 Help (6)
18 Artist's stand (5)
19 Pursues relentlessly (6)
21 Observe (3)
22 Mean and cowardly (9)

Down

1 Mimic (3)
2 Bedtime drink (5)
3 Let go (7)
4 Breathe in (6)
5 Sounds (6)
7 Sets off (9)
8 Invaluable (9)
12 Windpipe (7)
14 Shoved (6)
15 Large sea mammal (6)
17 Small military formation (5)
20 Period of time (3)

Across

1 Flightless bird (7)
5 Sway (4)
7 Ovum (3)
8 Riding breeches (8)
9 Detests (5)
10 Heinous (4)
13 Actor's part (4)
14 Genuine (4)
18 Badly off (4)
19 Mr Agassi, tennis star (5)
21 Partisan (3-5)
22 Epoch (3)
23 Eager (4)
24 As a whole (2,5)

Down

1 Overabundance (8)
2 Bedtime drink (8)
3 Unfair (6)
4 Pushes gently (6)
5 Mend (6)
6 Stopper (4)
11 Volume (8)
12 Demote (8)
15 Slacken (6)
16 Baby's bed (6)
17 Bicycle for two (6)
20 Formerly (4)

189

Across

1 Rural (6)
4 Male voice (5)
7 Sporting competition (10)
8 Adjoin (4)
9 Remains of a fire (5)
11 Patella (7)
13 Vocalists (7)
15 July, say (5)
17 Ruminant mammal (4)
18 Jobless (10)
20 Dark wood (5)
21 Acquire (6)

Down

1 Comment (6)
2 Steady brisk pace (4)
3 Capital of Venezuela (7)
4 Jewelled headdress (5)
5 Born (3)
6 Evaluates (5)
7 Adjust a radio (4,2)
10 Took notice of (6)
12 Musical instrument (7)
14 Sieve (6)
15 Rodent (5)
16 Cheerful (5)
17 Nimble, dexterous, etc. (4)
19 The self (3)

Across

1 Mild analgesic drug (11)
7 Cupid (4)
8 Fishing boat (7)
9 Be seated (3)
10 Flexible and supple (5)
11 Discount (6)
13 Cheroots, say (6)
16 Card suit (5)
18 Frozen water (3)
19 Crop-eating insects (7)
20 Boor (4)
21 Prudish or puritanical (6-5)

Down

1 Colour (6)
2 Country (6)
3 Cows, bulls, etc. (6)
4 Lag behind (5)
5 Civilian fighting force (7)
6 Pantries (7)
11 Recollects (7)
12 Cricket delivery (7)
13 Hand tool (6)
14 Celtic language (6)
15 Plump (6)
17 Japanese dish (5)

191

Across

1 Police photograph, informally (3,4)
7 Counting frame (6)
8 Disappoint (3,4)
9 Principal (4)
10 Performs (4)
12 Fix up (7)
14 Come down (7)
16 Dingy (4)
18 Tablet (4)
20 Blissful state (7)
21 Large blunt needle (6)
22 Entertainer (7)

Down

1 Duck type (7)
2 Gain access to (3,2)
3 Owl's cry (4)
4 Drinking vessel (7)
5 Agricultural worker (4,4)
6 Trip or excursion (6)
11 Similar (8)
12 Feeler (7)
13 Hug (7)
15 Newspaper boss (6)
17 Harvests (5)
19 Worry (4)

Across

1 Scientist's room (10)
6 Pamper (6)
7 Snares (5)
9 Private evening party (6)
10 Foot digit (3)
11 At the summit (4)
14 Sit for an artist (4)
15 Give a title to (3)
16 Irregular (6)
17 Stinks (5)
18 Cowardly (6)
20 Soft fluffy stuff (6,4)

Down

1 Zodiac sign (3)
2 Chesspiece (6)
3 Go back (6)
4 Move unsteadily (6)
5 Response (8)
6 Perforated pan (8)
8 Set of bones (8)
9 Hat with a wide brim (8)
12 Apple type (6)
13 Signal fire (6)
14 Pleasure craft (6)
19 Slippery fish (3)

193

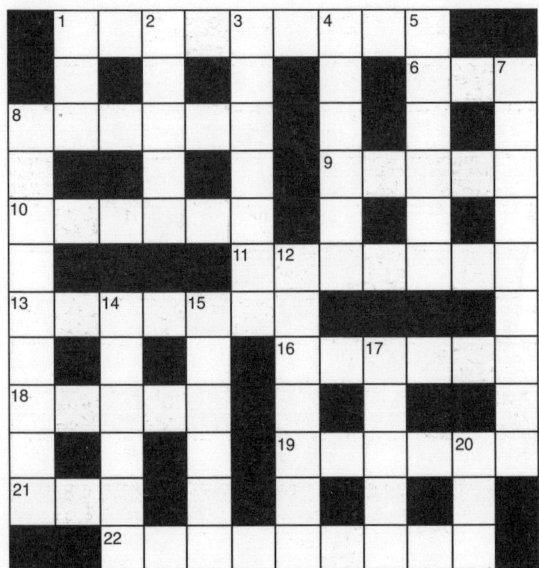

Across

1 Manacles (9)
6 Skill (3)
8 Batsman's posture (6)
9 Dutch cheese (5)
10 Aquatic reptile (6)
11 Chatters (7)
13 Flower-shaped badge (7)
16 Baby's toy (6)
18 Shinbone (5)
19 Homeless dogs (6)
21 Football's Mr Campbell (3)
22 Outstanding (9)

Down

1 Strike (3)
2 Group of nine (5)
3 Merciful (7)
4 Plane journey (6)
5 Acknowledge an officer (6)
7 Hands over (9)
8 Soaks (9)
12 Spray can (7)
14 Ingenious (6)
15 Mournful or pitiable (6)
17 Abrupt (5)
20 Nevertheless (3)

194

Across

1 Shipping hazard (7)
5 Wood type (4)
7 Enemy (3)
8 Garment with buttons (8)
9 Mother-of-pearl (5)
10 Enter (2,2)
13 Atmosphere (4)
14 Fling (4)
18 Deserve (4)
19 Very fat (5)
21 Scalp problem (8)
22 On strike (3)
23 Mr Hackman, actor (4)
24 Truthfulness (7)

Down

1 Boundless or endless (8)
2 Put into use (8)
3 Go beyond (6)
4 Car shed (6)
5 Petty details (6)
6 Slightly open (4)
11 Being many (8)
12 Obviously (8)
15 Rider's seat (6)
16 Sufficient (6)
17 Scientist, informally (6)
20 Urn (4)

195

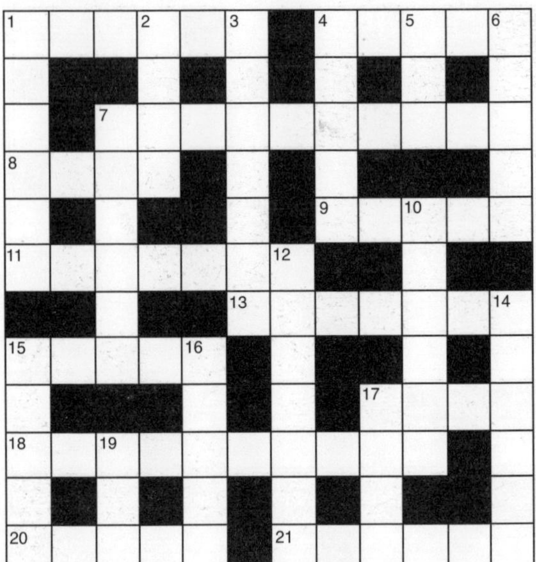

Across

1 Pungent bulb (6)
4 Wireless (5)
7 Valiant (10)
8 Stop (4)
9 School furniture items (5)
11 Funny drawing (7)
13 Nil (7)
15 Go in (5)
17 Scheme (4)
18 In a terrible rage (7,3)
20 Spools (5)
21 Add up to (6)

Down

1 Style of architecture (6)
2 Plunder (4)
3 Dead and rotting flesh (7)
4 Stiff (5)
5 Pair of performers (3)
6 Fertile spot (5)
7 Red wine (6)
10 Protect or guard (6)
12 Nine-sided figure (7)
14 Male goose (6)
15 Anaesthetic (5)
16 Horse controls (5)
17 Hand part (4)
19 Baked dish (3)

Across

1 On a small scale (2,9)
7 Box, in training (4)
8 Kills brutally (7)
9 Wrath (3)
10 Insect grub (5)
11 Sad or dull (6)
13 Powerful or strong (6)
16 Stadium (5)
18 Raised edge (3)
19 Behave without restraint (3,4)
20 Lazy (4)
21 Rich person (11)

Down

1 Damage or weaken (6)
2 Harbour for yachts (6)
3 That is to say (6)
4 Month (5)
5 Reveal or discover (7)
6 Rapture (7)
11 Drawing (7)
12 Everlasting (7)
13 Mr Scorsese, director (6)
14 Zodiac sign (6)
15 Dozen (6)
17 Defence plea (5)

Across

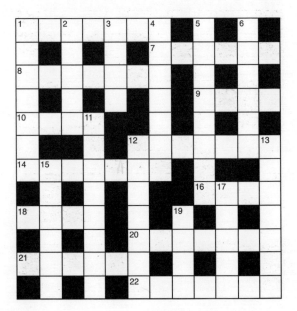

1 Male spouse (7)
7 A charm (6)
8 White of an egg (7)
9 Too (4)
10 Ticket money (4)
12 Trudge, informally (7)
14 Begins again (7)
16 Hitlerite (4)
18 Information (4)
20 Medium (7)
21 Choose (6)
22 Having died out (7)

Down

1 Go towards (4,3)
2 Not drunk (5)
3 Military land force (4)
4 Risks (7)
5 Of Europe and Asia (8)
6 Against (6)
11 Learned (8)
12 Having left a valid will (7)
13 Apparent (7)
15 Rubs out (6)
17 Once more (5)
19 Hotness (4)

Across

1 Salad dressing (10)
6 Deprive of food (6)
7 Uses one's eyes (5)
9 Noisy confused situation (6)
10 Biblical priest (3)
11 Rip (4)
14 Slender (4)
15 Flightless bird (3)
16 Expenditure (6)
17 Devil (5)
18 Suitable for crops (6)
20 Commercial (10)

Down

1 Covering for a floor (3)
2 Cricket delivery (6)
3 Stylus (6)
4 On fire (6)
5 Careless and untidy (8)
6 Immaculate (8)
8 Fellow sailor (8)
9 Long thin loaf (8)
12 High-quality brandy (6)
13 Stretch tight (6)
14 Jungle expedition (6)
19 Sheltered side (3)

199

Across

1 Made-up (9)
6 Organ of sight (3)
8 Road (6)
9 Sorcery (5)
10 Motive (6)
11 Spanish drink (7)
13 Nullifies (7)
16 Season (6)
18 Madagascan primate (5)
19 Unfastens (6)
21 Snow runner (3)
22 High wire (9)

Down

1 Excess flesh (3)
2 Salad garnish (5)
3 Concentrated (7)
4 Mr Mailer, author (6)
5 Accounts book (6)
7 Swaps (9)
8 Throttles (9)
12 Assail (7)
14 Opening move in chess (6)
15 Crowd (6)
17 Proportion (5)
20 Female sheep (3)

Across

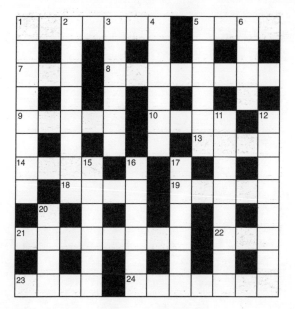

1 Food fish (7)
5 Unsightly (4)
7 Weep (3)
8 Wolfram (8)
9 Nervy (5)
10 Among (4)
13 Nap (4)
14 Skinny (4)
18 Romantic flower (4)
19 Mr Els, golfer (5)
21 Hit man (8)
22 In the past (3)
23 Makes mistakes (4)
24 Spotty disease (7)

Down

1 Pause in doubt (8)
2 Suave and refined (8)
3 Start or beginning (6)
4 American state (6)
5 Unspoken (6)
6 Sediment (4)
11 Failure or ruin (8)
12 Open-handed (8)
15 Wanderers (6)
16 Jettisoned cargo (6)
17 Rupture (6)
20 Operator (4)

SOLUTIONS

1

Across **1** Multitude **6** Car **8** Sponge **9** Ideas **10** Ferret **11** Iceland **13** Gradual **16** Ensign **18** Amble **19** Valise **21** Des **22** Hindrance
Down **1** Mop **2** Lunar **3** Inertia **4** Unwise **5** Eczema **7** Residence **8** Safeguard **12** Cleaver **14** Ambush **15** Uneven **17** Salon **20** See

2

Across **1** Scalpel **5** Film **7** Cue **8** Resolute **9** Roams **10** Rain **13** Poke **14** Tidy **18** Earl **19** Use up **21** Flamingo **22** Ire **23** Ewer **24** Targets
Down **1** Security **2** Adelaide **3** Perish **4** Lustre **5** Fillip **6** Lots **11** Nose dive **12** Helpless **15** Yammer **16** Planet **17** Humour **20** Slow

3

Across **1** Bistro **4** Enter **7** Peremptory **8** Amen **9** Legal **11** Secular **13** Perform **15** Piles **17** Lets **18** Undertaker **20** Pagan **21** Dancer
Down **1** Bleats **2** Then **3** Overlap **4** Expel **5** Too **6** Royal **7** Pencil **10** Glower **12** Red card **14** Master **15** Plump **16** Siren **17** Lean **19** Dig

4

Across **1** Downtrodden **7** Unit **8** Sustain **9** His **10** Sprig **11** Hybrid **13** Gammon **16** Mirth **18** Ted **19** Outcome **20** Erne **21** Kuala Lumpur
Down **1** Donkey **2** Wither **3** Tossed **4** Ousts **5** Diagram **6** Nonagon **11** Hammock **12** Biretta **13** Gateau **14** Made-up **15** Opener **17** Hoo-ha

5

Across **1** Plunder **7** Easter **8** Retreat **9** Erse **10** Slam **12** Publish **14** Lecture **16** Slur **18** Pair **20** Operate **21** Remark **22** Extinct
Down **1** Parasol **2** Ultra **3** Deep **4** Retinue **5** As well as **6** Census **11** Maternal **12** Provoke **13** Harvest **15** Enamel **17** Learn **19** Neat

6

Across **1** Rallycross **6** Agenda **7** Pleat **9** Dollar **10** Pal **11** Twin **14** Deer **15** Opt **16** Extras **17** Rinse **18** Import **20** Kettledrum
Down **1** Rag **2** London **3** Yearly **4** Report **5** Steeples **6** Abattoir **8** Tolerant **9** Distance **12** Detest **13** Strike **14** Dapper **19** Rum

7

Across **1** Frying pan **6** Air **8** Result **9** Stump **10** Single **11** Rashers **13** Baptism **16** Assume **18** Riles **19** Extols **21** Yet **22** Esperanto

Down **1** Foe **2** Young **3** Natters **4** Passes **5** Nature **7** Repossess **8** Raspberry **12** Amateur **14** Polite **15** Instep **17** Satin **20** Leo

8

Across **1** Pageant **5** Dirt **7** Eel **8** Activate **9** Hoist **10** Rout **13** Tine **14** Roll **18** Ease **19** Amend **21** Laudable **22** Ode **23** Star **24** Earnest

Down **1** Pie chart **2** Gullible **3** Awaits **4** Tutors **5** Devout **6** Rots **11** Tiresome **12** Dead heat **15** Ladder **16** Feeble **17** Career **20** Want

9

Across **1** Velour **4** Ideal **7** The gallows **8** True **9** Motto **11** Rebirth **13** Satchel **15** Theft **17** Wand **18** Politician **20** Dowel **21** Tennis

Down **1** Victor **2** Oche **3** Regrets **4** Islam **5** Ego **6** Lasso **7** Tumble **10** Tehran **12** Haricot **14** Ladies **15** Tepid **16** Total **17** Warn **19** Low

10

Across **1** Change hands **7** Scut **8** Sutures **9** Ass **10** Spume **11** Mock-up **13** Biceps **16** April **18** Lei **19** Origami **20** Sate **21** State of play

Down **1** Cuckoo **2** Attack **3** Gossip **4** Hates **5** Nurture **6** Systems **11** Meadows **12** Corsica **13** Belief **14** Chisel **15** Pantry **17** Lease

11

Across **1** Apostle **7** Noises **8** Premier **9** Item **10** Alto **12** Attends **14** Eclipse **16** Trim **18** Tutu **20** Unravel **21** Barren **22** Demotes

Down **1** Appease **2** Overt **3** Twig **4** En route **5** Diligent **6** Defend **11** Obituary **12** Astound **13** Samples **15** Cougar **17** Rivet **19** Brum

12

Across **1** Proportion **6** Static **7** Wasps **9** Pillar **10** Rye **11** Swat **14** Pest **15** Boa **16** Abacus **17** Exist **18** Tapers **20** Head-to-head

Down **1** Pet **2** Outfit **3** Occult **4** Thwart **5** Observes **6** Sensible **8** Shelters **9** Paradise **12** Wasted **13** Tattoo **14** Purple **19** Rod

13

Across **1** Collision **6** Out **8** Modest **9** Agile **10** Lesson **11** Satanic **13** Albumen **16** Castle **18** Kings **19** Equity **21** Eli **22** Turntable

Down **1** Coo **2** Leeks **3** Intense **4** Infant **5** Notion **7** Treachery **8** Milwaukee **12** Ancient **14** Bandit **15** Muster **17** Squib **20** The

14

Across **1** Baggage **5** Some **7** Ian **8** Secretly **9** Burst **10** Road **13** Wept **14** Note **18** Easy **19** Water **21** Snowball **22** Rue **23** Agog **24** Treason

Down **1** Brisbane **2** Generate **3** Assets **4** Encore **5** Seesaw **6** Mile **11** Dentures **12** Sturgeon **15** Earwig **16** Tyrant **17** Twelve **20** Snug

15

Across **1** Cuddle **4** Besom **7** Punch-drunk **8** Form **9** Earns **11** Ensures **13** Skipper **15** Tenor **17** Fact **18** Commercial **20** Types **21** Yorker

Down **1** Coffee **2** Drum **3** Escapes **4** Badge **5** Sou **6** Makes **7** Prison **10** Repeal **12** Sketchy **14** Rather **15** Tacit **16** Reeks **17** Fair **19** Map

16

Across **1** Seasickness **7** Clot **8** Flipper **9** Ava **10** Event **11** Mighty **13** Roasts **16** Cones **18** Act **19** Aerosol **20** Hide **21** Lollipop man

Down **1** Saluki **2** Attach **3** Infamy **4** Knife **5** Express **6** Sprites **11** Michael **12** General **13** Rialto **14** Anthem **15** Tendon **17** Sushi

17

Across **1** Cry wolf **7** Adroit **8** Abandon **9** Shut **10** Kite **12** Arsenal **14** Reverse **16** Stir **18** Grin **20** Routine **21** Agatha **22** Settees

Down **1** Cracker **2** Yeast **3** Odds **4** Fanfare **5** Brussels **6** Fibula **11** Eternity **12** As far as **13** Larders **15** Enrage **17** Twice **19** Rust

18

Across **1** Floodlight **6** Otters **7** Eclat **9** Bolero **10** Ova **11** Tarn **14** Beta **15** Era **16** Afraid **17** Tooth **18** Thirst **20** Attraction

Down **1** Fit **2** Oregon **3** Duster **4** Icebox **5** Hallowed **6** Ointment **8** To a fault **9** Break out **12** Lather **13** Critic **14** Bikini **19** Sin

19

Across **1** Bellicose **6** Dip **8** Stitch **9** Amber **10** Proper **11** Iceberg **13** Elevate **16** Russia **18** Bytes **19** Afresh **21** Roe **22** Man and boy

Down **1** Bat **2** Let up **3** Inherit **4** Of late **5** Edible **7** Paragraph **8** September **12** Certain **14** Esteem **15** Assign **17** Scrub **20** Sly

20

Across **1** Serving **5** Bald **7** Rim **8** Demolish **9** Price **10** Noon **13** Nail **14** Even **18** Dare **19** Ocean **21** Vibrates **22** Ewe **23** Claw **24** Resists

Down **1** Shrapnel **2** Remained **3** Indeed **4** Gemini **5** Bolton **6** Lisp **11** Nameless **12** Blunders **15** Narrow **16** Better **17** Boasts **20** Dial

21

Across **1** Banger **4** Rumba **7** Marvellous **8** Lead **9** Cabin **11** Pull out **13** Erratic **15** Extra **17** Toad **18** Contrition **20** Latin **21** Rascal

Down **1** Burlap **2** Glad **3** Revenue **4** Relic **5** Moo **6** Arson **7** Mallet **10** Button **12** Tractor **14** Cudgel **15** Excel **16** Apron **17** Tots **19** Net

22

Across **1** Funambulist **7** Imam **8** Supreme **9** Age **10** React **11** Ceases **13** Bustle **16** Mates **18** Jar **19** Oregano **20** Eden **21** Empty-headed

Down **1** Famine **2** Nomads **3** Misers **4** Upper **5** Inexact **6** Theatre **11** Compose **12** Antwerp **13** By Jove **14** Shrewd **15** Legend **17** Scary

23

Across **1** Peckish **7** Editor **8** Arizona **9** Skid **10** Ayes **12** Barrage **14** Destroy **16** Pail **18** Garb **20** Creates **21** Attune **22** Returns

Down **1** Placard **2** Crime **3** Iron **4** Hearsay **5** Airstrip **6** Boxing **11** Set about **12** Bouncer **13** Enlists **15** Ecarte **17** Alter **19** Beat

24

Across **1** Invincible **6** Bedlam **7** North **9** Pellet **10** Son **11** Flat **14** Hugs **15** Gel **16** Prefer **17** Tense **18** Mottle **20** Repeatedly

Down **1** Ice **2** Velvet **3** Namely **4** Ignite **5** Larkspur **6** Bun fight **8** Handsome **9** Parlance **12** Sphere **13** Permit **14** Heated **19** Lay

25

Across **1** Persevere **6** Nip **8** Behind **9** Spice **10** Endear **11** Sisters **13** Enemies **16** Option **18** Pipes **19** Adapts **21** Run **22** Desperate

Down **1** Pie **2** Raise **3** Endorse **4** Erases **5** Engine **7** Pheasants **8** Beekeeper **12** Isolate **14** Expend **15** Issues **17** Tiara **20** Toe

26

Across **1** Receipt **5** Salt **7** Lap **8** Peaceful **9** Gloss **10** Colt **13** Sumo **14** Term **18** Daze **19** Rinse **21** Ordinary **22** Ore **23** Here **24** Denotes

Down **1** Relegate **2** Cupboard **3** Impish **4** Thatch **5** Smells **6** Loud **11** Turncoat **12** Homeless **15** Malice **16** Demand **17** Crayon **20** Urge

27

Across **1** Sahara **4** Kevin **7** Hook and eye **8** Neon **9** Seems **11** Concord **13** Drastic **15** Catch **17** Bran **18** Mysterious **20** Curls **21** Gander

Down **1** Scenic **2** Anon **3** Awkward **4** Kinds **5** Vie **6** Needs **7** Hornet **10** Enters **12** Drawing **14** Cancer **15** Comic **16** Heeds **17** Burn **19** Sir

28

Across **1** Microscopic **7** Also **8** Enlarge **9** Inn **10** Singe **11** Shield **13** Despot **16** Atlas **18** Hip **19** Leg-pull **20** Espy **21** Welsh rabbit

Down **1** Mulish **2** Choice **3** Opened **4** Cells **5** Parsnip **6** Clement **11** Swallow **12** Illegal **13** Dahlia **14** Superb **15** Output **17** South

29

Across **1** Quartet **7** Rub out **8** Asinine **9** Oboe **10** Rash **12** Slumber **14** Lettuce **16** Loaf **18** Shoe **20** Termite **21** Gentle **22** Resents

Down **1** Quarrel **2** Alias **3** Thin **4** Tremble **5** Abnormal **6** Europe **11** Hitherto **12** Scatter **13** Rafters **15** Echoes **17** Onion **19** Errs

30

Across **1** Coconut shy **6** Hermit **7** Tests **9** Coyote **10** Too **11** Darn **14** Snap **15** Ham **16** Avocet **17** Pants **18** Steven **20** Elementary

Down **1** Cue **2** Common **3** Nation **4** Tether **5** Hesitant **6** Hardship **8** Scorpion **9** Criminal **12** Ransom **13** Poison **14** Serena **19** Ely

31

Across **1** Aborigine **6** Lip **8** Beacon **9** Gavel **10** Terror **11** Essence **13** Expense **16** Cravat **18** First **19** Isobar **21** Yes **22** Engineers
Down **1** Axe **2** Occur **3** Ignores **4** Images **5** Eleven **7** Polyester **8** Butterfly **12** Section **14** Peruse **15** Nutmeg **17** Adore **20** Ass

32

Across **1** Cagoule **5** Soda **7** Lea **8** Carnival **9** Aisle **10** Keep **13** Ruth **14** Leaf **18** Wise **19** Locum **21** Beginner **22** Ail **23** Lash **24** Letters
Down **1** Culpable **2** Glass jaw **3** Uncles **4** Eureka **5** Spider **6** Dear **11** Purchase **12** Shambles **15** Finish **16** Fennel **17** Claret **20** Beta

33

Across **1** Father **4** Lance **7** Particular **8** Clap **9** Dunce **11** Scarlet **13** Sextant **15** Weeps **17** Plan **18** Dictionary **20** Night **21** Sudden
Down **1** Fracas **2** Heap **3** Rotates **4** Lucid **5** Nil **6** Eerie **7** Palace **10** Nearly **12** Tetanus **14** Tendon **15** Widen **16** Swift **17** Prod **19** Cog

34

Across **1** Accelerates **7** Gene **8** Crevice **9** Emu **10** Sleet **11** Lament **13** Goatee **16** Tiles **18** Leo **19** Literal **20** Ruin **21** Plain-spoken
Down **1** Agenda **2** Cheese **3** Locust **4** Reels **5** Trident **6** Spectre **11** Let slip **12** Militia **13** Gallop **14** Anorak **15** Ensign **17** Siren

35

Across **1** Halibut **7** Annual **8** Cardiac **9** Face **10** Omen **12** Hurling **14** Snorkel **16** Stet **18** Huge **20** Granite **21** Pedalo **22** Nestles
Down **1** Hectors **2** Large **3** Brie **4** Tactful **5** Snaffles **6** Falcon **11** Norseman **12** Hexagon **13** Gathers **15** Nausea **17** Twirl **19** Lass

36

Across **1** Vocabulary **6** Excite **7** Tinge **9** Talons **10** Gap **11** Alex **14** Odin **15** Get **16** Arcane **17** Tacit **18** Elopes **20** Determined
Down **1** Vex **2** Climax **3** Breton **4** Latest **5** Renegade **6** Escargot **8** Expunges **9** Tentacle **12** Rattle **13** Scream **14** On loan **19** End

37

Across **1** Economics **6** Tut **8** String **9** Atoll **10** Tavern **11** Integer **13** Advance **16** Govern **18** Ideal **19** Thrice **21** Nun **22** Assessors

Down **1** Eat **2** Olive **3** Organic **4** Infant **5** Strong **7** Tolerance **8** Situation **12** Negates **14** Vienna **15** Nylons **17** Virgo **20** Cos

38

Across **1** Edibles **5** Push **7** Top **8** Talented **9** Maize **10** Tail **13** Tone **14** Trot **18** Neat **19** Rules **21** Swastika **22** Pro **23** Onus **24** Example

Down **1** Estimate **2** Imprison **3** Latter **4** Splits **5** Pundit **6** Step **11** Lollipop **12** Gemstone **15** Teases **16** Strike **17** Armada **20** Ewan

39

Across **1** That is **4** Biped **7** Horizontal **8** Deal **9** Horde **11** Measles **13** Resumes **15** Thaws **17** Tutu **18** Malefactor **20** Deter **21** Silver

Down **1** Tandem **2** Tool **3** Snigger **4** Booth **5** Pot **6** Delve **7** Havana **10** Rumour **12** Selects **14** Stupor **15** Timid **16** So far **17** Toil **19** Lot

40

Across **1** Fool's errand **7** Edit **8** Hatchet **9** Woe **10** Reeks **11** Castle **13** Caress **16** Inner **18** Mob **19** Notable **20** Ulna **21** Immediately

Down **1** Fedora **2** Outwit **3** Scheme **4** Rotor **5** Achieve **6** Detests **11** Chianti **12** Sanctum **13** Camera **14** Rebuke **15** Skinny **17** Rabid

41

Across **1** Abolish **7** Obtain **8** Chicken **9** Else **10** Item **12** At a push **14** Nursery **16** Stag **18** Asia **20** Thimble **21** Renege **22** Remnant

Down **1** Auction **2** On ice **3** Irks **4** Honesty **5** Attempts **6** Kisses **11** Mistakes **12** Arbiter **13** Highest **15** Ulster **17** Tibia **19** Firm

42

Across **1** Follow suit **6** Hernia **7** Cuffs **9** Remote **10** Rue **11** Grit **14** Soot **15** Two **16** Author **17** Noose **18** Enrols **20** Assortment

Down **1** Foe **2** Lancet **3** Orator **4** Sacred **5** Inferior **6** Heighten **8** Sweaters **9** Rigorous **12** Take to **13** Street **14** Source **19** Lit

43

Across **1** Ludicrous **6** Ava **8** Decide **9** Crawl **10** Silent **11** Ostrich **13** Popcorn **16** Indium **18** Evict **19** E-mails **21** Rut **22** Head start
Down **1** Lee **2** Drive **3** Creator **4** Offcut **5** Safari **7** All thumbs **8** Disappear **12** Snipers **14** Plinth **15** Ottawa **17** Drama **20** Let

44

Across **1** Blatant **5** Erse **7** Nod **8** Mackerel **9** Inter **10** Last **13** Ouzo **14** Look **18** Nape **19** Angel **21** Apiarist **22** Tap **23** Once **24** Strange
Down **1** Bone idle **2** Audition **3** Admire **4** Tackle **5** Even so **6** Shed **11** Tungsten **12** Collapse **15** Karate **16** Begins **17** Batter **20** Spin

45

Across **1** Bottom **4** Wigan **7** Castigates **8** Stop **9** Natal **11** Singers **13** Saffron **15** Basic **17** Talc **18** Estimation **20** Dogma **21** Roster
Down **1** Bursts **2** Trap **3** Meteors **4** Wagon **5** Got **6** Nasal **7** Counts **10** Turban **12** Saunter **14** Nectar **15** Breed **16** Comma **17** Toss **19** Tag

46

Across **1** Destination **7** Knee **8** Trapeze **9** Ace **10** Stall **11** Closet **13** Tokens **16** Llama **18** See **19** Ominous **20** Pike **21** Fundamental
Down **1** Dental **2** Shears **3** Intent **4** Amass **5** Iterate **6** Needles **11** Call off **12** Ovation **13** Tussle **14** Keep at **15** Nickel **17** Aroma

47

Across **1** Wyoming **7** Exempt **8** Dungeon **9** Aunt **10** Whet **12** Snooker **14** Retinue **16** Edam **18** Iron **20** Asunder **21** Violin **22** Austere
Down **1** Widower **2** Ounce **3** Idea **4** Genuine **5** Let alone **6** Sponge **11** Triangle **12** Sultana **13** Remorse **15** Earwig **17** Dodge **19** Fuss

48

Across **1** Sweetheart **6** Impair **7** Tales **9** Feline **10** Ski **11** Idol **14** Reps **15** Art **16** Uranus **17** Exact **18** Ethics **20** All-rounder
Down **1** Sum **2** Enamel **3** Turnip **4** Either **5** Relishes **6** Indicate **8** Scissors **9** Football **12** Butter **13** Gateau **14** Rushed **19** Cur

49

Across **1** Mint sauce **6** Lei **8** Sprint **9** Rupee **10** As well **11** Element **13** En masse **16** Arabic **18** Owner **19** Normal **21** Tug **22** Entertain

Down **1** Map **2** Naive **3** Settles **4** Untrue **5** Elapse **7** Identical **8** Scapegoat **12** Learner **14** Manage **15** Strict **17** Aorta **20** Ann

50

Across **1** Abridge **5** Oast **7** Gin **8** Nonsense **9** Leeds **10** Slam **13** Site **14** Noun **18** Pair **19** Agree **21** Belittle **22** Ire **23** Hype **24** Lottery

Down **1** Angelina **2** Runner-up **3** Danish **4** Ernest **5** Operas **6** So-so **11** Migraine **12** Cemetery **15** Native **16** Brutal **17** Latent **20** Very

51

Across **1** All but **4** Cigar **7** Backgammon **8** Heat **9** Spoon **11** Alfalfa **13** Freedom **15** Cheap **17** Fret **18** Nutritious **20** Eyrie **21** Salver

Down **1** Asthma **2** Brat **3** Take off **4** Chars **5** Gum **6** Ronan **7** Baffle **10** Orders **12** Armpits **14** Mother **15** Canoe **16** Pride **17** Full **19** Tor

52

Across **1** Double Dutch **7** Alas **8** Cleaver **9** Era **10** Serve **11** Prance **13** Savant **16** Goods **18** Pal **19** Extract **20** Inch **21** Thoughtless

Down **1** Dollar **2** Unseen **3** Locate **4** Deeds **5** Taverna **6** Harvest **11** Pigment **12** About to **13** Septet **14** Valise **15** Nieces **17** Slang

53

Across **1** Embargo **7** Beetle **8** Updates **9** Rust **10** Apes **12** Prepare **14** Equable **16** Tees **18** Limb **20** Theatre **21** Hearse **22** Refrain

Down **1** Educate **2** Badge **3** Rate **4** Obscure **5** Decrepit **6** Closer **11** Scabbard **12** Plotter **13** Eastern **15** Quiver **17** Extra **19** Beef

54

Across **1** Disgusting **6** Rector **7** Ratio **9** Molars **10** Fin **11** Adam **14** Perm **15** Tar **16** Otters **17** Exams **18** Defeat **20** Helicopter

Down **1** Doe **2** Sitcom **3** Uproar **4** Thrush **5** Notifies **6** Repartee **8** Ointment **9** Marriage **12** Bonsai **13** Studio **14** Profit **19** Air

55

Across **1** Liverpool **6** Apt **8** Benign **9** Grows **10** Season **11** Tantrum **13** Abandon **16** Ticket **18** Dirge **19** Enmesh **21** Roe **22** Destroyer
Down **1** Lie **2** Veins **3** Run into **4** Origin **5** Labour **7** Test match **8** Bystander **12** Ant bear **14** Air bed **15** Dreads **17** Comfy **20** Sir

56

Across **1** Publish **5** Snow **7** Eat **8** Vindaloo **9** Evens **10** Stab **13** Norm **14** Taut **18** Pile **19** Ether **21** Budapest **22** Mel **23** Stye **24** Teeters
Down **1** Presents **2** Butter up **3** Invest **4** Honest **5** Seaman **6** Oboe **11** Bonhomie **12** Emeralds **15** Tirade **16** Decent **17** Settee **20** Hunt

57

Across **1** Static **4** Beret **7** Jolly Roger **8** Abut **9** Erase **11** Hopeful **13** Sausage **15** Birds **17** Feel **18** Scandalous **20** Specs **21** Nudist
Down **1** Splash **2** Toot **3** Callous **4** Barge **5** Rug **6** Terse **7** Jumper **10** Abates **12** Lanolin **14** Enlist **15** Basic **16** Sides **17** Fund **19** Awe

58

Across **1** Greasepaint **7** Bloc **8** Chortle **9** Ash **10** Shred **11** Ardent **13** Grumpy **16** Opals **18** Ill **19** Harpoon **20** Oval **21** Roman candle
Down **1** Golfer **2** Escape **3** Sachet **4** Pious **5** Interim **6** Tuesday **11** Another **12** Diagram **13** Guinea **14** Unload **15** Palate **17** Scorn

59

Across **1** Boredom **7** Adroit **8** Ignites **9** Whip **10** Ties **12** Average **14** Elusive **16** Text **18** Idle **20** Amiable **21** Ceased **22** Observe
Down **1** Brittle **2** Rinse **3** Date **4** Massive **5** Brown rat **6** Viking **11** Suspense **12** Avocado **13** Extreme **15** Ladder **17** Ember **19** Hiss

60

Across **1** Letter bomb **6** Spring **7** Igloo **9** Dogleg **10** Nod **11** Peer **14** Mean **15** Eye **16** Antler **17** Shark **18** Rarely **20** Reinforces
Down **1** Lap **2** Tailor **3** Engulf **4** Bridge **5** Malinger **6** Stoppers **8** Ordinary **9** Delegate **12** Napkin **13** Stereo **14** Metric **19** Les

61

Across **1** Extensive **6** Cod **8** Moment **9** Girls **10** Kettle **11** Rashers **13** Suggest **16** Little **18** Inset **19** Nimbus **21** Toe **22** Dismantle
Down **1** Ego **2** Trent **3** Natters **4** Images **5** Ecarte **7** Disasters **8** Makeshift **12** Atlanta **14** Gasped **15** Enters **17** Tempt **20** Use

62

Across **1** Boffins **5** Raft **7** Gnu **8** Barefoot **9** Utter **10** Will **13** Earl **14** Grin **18** Note **19** Agent **21** Shamrock **22** Die **23** Anon **24** Retires
Down **1** Begrudge **2** Fountain **3** Inborn **4** Shrewd **5** Raffle **6** Frog **11** Lavender **12** Flutters **15** Norman **16** Devour **17** Packet **20** Shin

63

Across **1** Angora **4** Bagel **7** Hullabaloo **8** Odes **9** Yanks **11** Barring **13** Toddler **15** Trend **17** Snap **18** Capricious **20** Thank **21** Gather
Down **1** Absorb **2** Onus **3** Ailment **4** Bobby **5** Gel **6** Loots **7** Hearse **10** Nylons **12** Gosling **14** Repair **15** Tacit **16** Drink **17** Suet **19** Pea

64

Across **1** Into thin air **7** Fist **8** Mallard **9** Tub **10** Renal **11** Become **13** Status **16** Sharp **18** Eft **19** Umpires **20** Able **21** Tiddlywinks
Down **1** Icicle **2** Tattoo **3** Tumble **4** Idler **5** Against **6** Riddles **11** Biscuit **12** Clapped **13** Seesaw **14** Attain **15** Uncles **17** Peril

65

Across **1** Locusts **7** Knives **8** Private **9** Moat **10** Imam **12** Phantom **14** Gangway **16** Suds **18** Epic **20** Neptune **21** Savage **22** Royalty
Down **1** Lapwing **2** China **3** Stay **4** Sketchy **5** Diamonds **6** Pedalo **11** Magician **12** Partner **13** Mystery **15** Appear **17** Usual **19** Spry

66

Across **1** Eradicates **6** Ground **7** Deems **9** Delete **10** Hoe **11** Amen **14** Knit **15** Ice **16** Not out **17** Miami **18** Pagans **20** Wanderlust
Down **1** Ear **2** Acumen **3** Indeed **4** Andrew **5** Elephant **6** Geranium **8** Shelters **9** Demerara **12** Unkind **13** Stupor **14** Kung fu **19** Net

67

Across **1** On the trot **6** Act **8** Defend **9** Arena **10** Border **11** Salutes **13** Trainer **16** Rattle **18** Being **19** Spirit **21** Ewe **22** So to speak
Down **1** Ore **2** Tread **3** Endorse **4** Recall **5** Talent **7** Transient **8** Debatable **12** Arrests **14** Abides **15** Nugget **17** Twice **20** Ink

68

Across **1** Fallacy **5** Tots **7** Art **8** Bungalow **9** Reeks **10** Exit **13** Coin **14** Nile **18** Yarn **19** Clear **21** Pedigree **22** Dip **23** Stay **24** Steered
Down **1** Flagrant **2** Latterly **3** Ambush **4** Yonder **5** Tragic **6** Tool **11** Toreador **12** Intrepid **15** Easily **16** Snores **17** Accede **20** Pest

69

Across **1** Amidst **4** Gamma **7** Four-poster **8** Chap **9** Spain **11** Stamina **13** Traitor **15** Scent **17** Fact **18** Additional **20** Ernie **21** Sordid
Down **1** Abacus **2** Drop **3** Torment **4** Gross **5** Mat **6** Apron **7** Facade **10** Astral **12** Arduous **14** Rotund **15** Spade **16** Title **17** Fair **19** Din

70

Across **1** Broad-minded **7** Plea **8** Treacle **9** The **10** Lords **11** Boasts **13** Summer **16** Niche **18** Ike **19** Unaware **20** Scar **21** Tickled pink
Down **1** Bolero **2** Orates **3** Deters **4** Ideal **5** Decorum **6** Dresser **11** Banquet **12** Archaic **13** Shield **14** Muesli **15** Embark **17** E-mail

71

Across **1** Rostrum **7** Evades **8** Laggard **9** Hard **10** Pits **12** Balloon **14** Eternal **16** Rear **18** Oven **20** Inferno **21** Credit **22** Shrieks
Down **1** Relapse **2** Sight **3** Real **4** Medical **5** Bachelor **6** Near to **11** Serenade **12** Bandits **13** Nervous **15** Tavern **17** Eerie **19** Afar

72

Across **1** Wilderness **6** Ignore **7** Turns **9** Easter **10** Sue **11** Fish **14** Feed **15** Tea **16** Adonis **17** Digit **18** Dainty **20** Strengthen
Down **1** Wig **2** Loofah **3** Events **4** Nature **5** Stresses **6** Ill-fated **8** Speedway **9** Escargot **12** Battle **13** Hot dog **14** Finish **19** Tin

73
Across **1** Daredevil **6** Eat **8** Before **9** Shine **10** United **11** Essence **13** Elegant **16** Ever so **18** Aside **19** Notice **21** Dim **22** Assembles
Down **1** Due **2** Roost **3** Dresden **4** Versus **5** Lesion **7** Therefore **8** Boulevard **12** Sternum **14** Enigma **15** Agents **17** Extol **20** Cos

74
Across **1** Chicago **5** Beta **7** Rim **8** Addition **9** Fatal **10** Acid **13** Nice **14** Earn **18** Ease **19** Gouda **21** Alsatian **22** Get **23** Beam **24** Meander
Down **1** Carefree **2** Immature **3** Arable **4** Ordeal **5** Butt in **6** Trot **11** Divulged **12** Decanter **15** Napalm **16** Medium **17** Agenda **20** Flee

75
Across **1** Ballad **4** Taper **7** Fascinates **8** Bran **9** Class **11** Rainbow **13** Natural **15** Beech **17** Span **18** Broadsheet **20** Ewers **21** Permit
Down **1** Barber **2** Lean **3** Decagon **4** Tunic **5** Pot **6** Roses **7** Famine **10** Abrupt **12** Warship **14** Lancet **15** Bible **16** Hides **17** Sear **19** One

76
Across **1** Crack of dawn **7** Kiwi **8** Sprites **9** Sum **10** Excel **11** Planet **13** Wavers **16** Acres **18** Rio **19** Also-ran **20** Lead **21** Dilapidated
Down **1** Chisel **2** Alison **3** Kismet **4** Force **5** Article **6** Nestles **11** Placard **12** Aerosol **13** Warned **14** Violet **15** Regard **17** Strap

77
Across **1** Exhibit **7** Equips **8** Largest **9** Brew **10** Pier **12** Durable **14** Enemies **16** Dais **18** Etch **20** Neither **21** Doomed **22** Sutures
Down **1** Eclipse **2** Horse **3** Beef **4** Tetanus **5** Cupboard **6** Appeal **11** Romp home **12** Demands **13** Ensures **15** Notion **17** Abhor **19** Mist

78
Across **1** Dishearten **6** Recent **7** Put up **9** Pieces **10** Roc **11** Talc **14** Bail **15** Rat **16** Abseil **17** Canoe **18** Editor **20** Impression
Down **1** Dye **2** Scenic **3** Entice **4** Repose **5** External **6** Rhetoric **8** Peculiar **9** Platinum **12** Career **13** Assess **14** Bikini **19** Own

79

Across **1** Blackmail **6** Imp **8** Ensign **9** Hotel **10** Fleece **11** Laments **13** Confess **16** Salami **18** Eider **19** Urgent **21** Tee **22** Spectator
Down **1** Ban **2** Afire **3** Kennels **4** Anthem **5** Listen **7** Polo shirt **8** Efficient **12** Assault **14** Nudges **15** Enrage **17** Light **20** Nor

80

Across **1** Ability **5** Afro **7** Eli **8** Heat wave **9** Drawl **10** Lays **13** So-so **14** Eyes **18** Sail **19** Tribe **21** Tug-of-war **22** Urn **23** Seer **24** Pioneer
Down **1** Aberdeen **2** Imitates **3** Inhale **4** Yearly **5** Always **6** Rave **11** Solitude **12** Governor **15** Savour **16** Blow up **17** Stereo **20** Huge

81

Across **1** Cosmos **4** Brave **7** Fastidious **8** Roll **9** Trace **11** Hamster **13** Lenient **15** Style **17** Sumo **18** Inevitable **20** Sabot **21** Expend
Down **1** Church **2** Meal **3** Satchel **4** Bidet **5** Ado **6** Ensue **7** Flimsy **10** Avenue **12** Release **14** Tooted **15** Spins **16** Evict **17** Slap **19** Ebb

82

Across **1** Illuminates **7** Fuss **8** Stripes **9** Sot **10** Erode **11** Banner **13** Closet **16** Octet **18** Dot **19** Sibling **20** Lair **21** Meet halfway
Down **1** Iguana **2** Lesson **3** Master **4** Nerve **5** Tiptoes **6** Suspect **11** Blossom **12** Notable **13** Cudgel **14** Outlaw **15** Enmity **17** Thigh

83

Across **1** Gazelle **7** Nearly **8** Amongst **9** Eros **10** Gust **12** Illness **14** Winsome **16** Tugs **18** Want **20** Inertia **21** Bobbin **22** Echelon
Down **1** Glasgow **2** Zooms **3** Legs **4** Entitle **5** Hazelnut **6** Allots **11** Test tube **12** Imagine **13** Sustain **15** In a row **17** Until **19** Mesh

84

Across **1** Handspring **6** Gentle **7** Nomad **9** Sorrow **10** Tut **11** Eden **14** Sewn **15** Opt **16** Cancer **17** Suede **18** Innate **20** Stationery
Down **1** Hoe **2** Nation **3** Sherry **4** Renown **5** No matter **6** Generous **8** Detonate **9** Seat belt **12** Accent **13** Indigo **14** Seance **19** Try

85

Across **1** Notorious **6** Out **8** Remand **9** Raise **10** Clinic **11** Assumes **13** Patella **16** Lather **18** Idiot **19** Ambles **21** Nil **22** Stalemate

Down **1** Nee **2** Train **3** Radical **4** Operas **5** Sodium **7** Treasures **8** Reception **12** Salvage **14** Twirls **15** Latvia **17** Tibia **20** Eve

86

Across **1** Depress **5** Hock **7** Rue **8** Breeding **9** Mince **10** Ties **13** None **14** Nuns **18** Tone **19** Icing **21** Manacles **22** Bet **23** Shoe **24** Western

Down **1** Dortmund **2** Pregnant **3** Emblem **4** Siesta **5** Hidden **6** Cone **11** Sociable **12** Heighten **15** Solace **16** Yellow **17** Kisses **20** Cash

87

Across **1** Critic **4** Sleet **7** Flamboyant **8** Abel **9** Recur **11** Amateur **13** Seaweed **15** Theft **17** Mess **18** Whatsoever **20** Rupee **21** Tender

Down **1** Canada **2** Till **3** Cumulus **4** Spoor **5** Era **6** Tutor **7** Female **10** Clever **12** Respect **14** Duster **15** Tower **16** Taste **17** Mean **19** Asp

88

Across **1** Bad-tempered **7** Knit **8** Run into **9** Axe **10** Chase **11** Faints **13** Tackle **16** Oasis **18** Set **19** Selects **20** Nags **21** Minesweeper

Down **1** Banana **2** Detain **3** Egress **4** Panic **5** Ransack **6** Diocese **11** Flotsam **12** Insulin **13** Tussle **14** Catnap **15** Logger **17** Sects

89

Across **1** Javelin **7** Oliver **8** All ears **9** Oust **10** Odds **12** Sawdust **14** Secrecy **16** Rota **18** Ache **20** Fragile **21** Reveal **22** Embassy

Down **1** Jealous **2** Valid **3** Leak **4** Nosegay **5** Disorder **6** Census **11** Sorcerer **12** Scuffle **13** Tragedy **15** Exceed **17** Omits **19** Lamb

90

Across **1** Peashooter **6** Infect **7** Plump **9** Cheers **10** Ago **11** Idea **14** Peep **15** Ode **16** Ironed **17** Shove **18** Puppet **20** By and large

Down **1** Pun **2** Aretha **3** Hatred **4** Oppose **5** Educated **6** Illinois **8** Prospect **9** Ceremony **12** Pigeon **13** Compel **14** Pepper **19** Ewe

91

Across **1** Dramatist **6** Wig **8** Reject **9** Ellen **10** Tendon **11** Natters **13** Logical **16** Goatee **18** Among **19** Edicts **21** Egg **22** Excessive
Down **1** Die **2** Ahead **3** Antenna **4** Invent **5** Twelve **7** Gangsters **8** Retaliate **12** Algiers **14** George **15** Cognac **17** Alibi **20** Toe

92

Across **1** Caprice **5** Tutu **7** Ass **8** Critical **9** Point **10** Lash **13** Tile **14** Ogle **18** Yard **19** Pedal **21** Bull's-eye **22** Oar **23** Thus **24** Berates
Down **1** Champion **2** Possibly **3** Incite **4** Edible **5** Thirst **6** Trap **11** Hindmost **12** Declares **15** Eagles **16** Adverb **17** Appear **20** Push

93

Across **1** Bitter **4** Sweat **7** Grass roots **8** Tray **9** Burly **11** Rodents **13** Shatter **15** Banjo **17** Loam **18** Now and then **20** Haste **21** Notify
Down **1** Batter **2** Tory **3** Resists **4** Scrub **5** Ego **6** Testy **7** Garden **10** Ration **12** Shorten **14** Remedy **15** Bench **16** Ounce **17** Left **19** Was

94

Across **1** Rubber-stamp **7** Fall **8** Dentist **9** Lie **10** White **11** Answer **13** Comedy **16** Thaws **18** Sir **19** Rule out **20** Girl **21** Down-to-earth
Down **1** Reason **2** Bellow **3** Endear **4** Sinew **5** Asinine **6** Pottery **11** Altered **12** Shallow **13** Castle **14** Merger **15** Dearth **17** Shoot

95

Across **1** Beneath **7** Ignore **8** Rebound **9** Also **10** Ayes **12** Success **14** Kidnaps **16** Stun **18** Idol **20** Nurture **21** Rescue **22** Riposte
Down **1** Barrack **2** Noble **3** Ague **4** Hideous **5** Enhances **6** Crisis **11** Sunblock **12** Spanner **13** Sincere **15** Indeed **17** Thugs **19** Trip

96

Across **1** Foundation **6** Utopia **7** Roses **9** Breeze **10** Roe **11** Ogre **14** Nest **15** Man **16** Issues **17** Natal **18** Across **20** Before long
Down **1** Fit **2** Umpire **3** Draper **4** Target **5** Observes **6** Uncommon **8** Spectres **9** Brunette **12** Rialto **13** Estate **14** Near to **19** Sag

97

Across **1** Immediate **6** Low **8** Slight **9** David **10** One-two **11** Intense **13** Pollute **16** Glared **18** Exams **19** Employ **21** Sea **22** Sceptical
Down **1** Ill **2** Might **3** Detroit **4** Amidst **5** Eleven **7** Wednesday **8** Stop press **12** Neglect **14** Llamas **15** Ursine **17** Aspic **20** Oil

98

Across **1** Cajoles **5** Gale **7** Mat **8** Tolerate **9** Seize **10** Odin **13** Cain **14** Loot **18** Nose **19** Elite **21** Daffodil **22** Ace **23** Gene **24** Earnest
Down **1** Camisole **2** Jettison **3** Litter **4** Saloon **5** Garlic **6** Lots **11** Navigate **12** Interest **15** Toffee **16** Needle **17** Cellar **20** Save

99

Across **1** Fickle **4** Cites **7** Methodical **8** Leap **9** Titan **11** Coronet **13** Satsuma **15** Fudge **17** Hunt **18** Encourages **20** Habit **21** Debris
Down **1** Frolic **2** Keep **3** Exhales **4** Cadet **5** Tic **6** Salon **7** Madrid **10** Taurus **12** Tankard **14** Actors **15** Fresh **16** Erupt **17** Herb **19** Cob

100

Across **1** Industrious **7** Oven **8** Lecture **9** Tea **10** Sheep **11** Really **13** Rustle **16** Pours **18** Sol **19** Attends **20** Item **21** Secret agent
Down **1** Invite **2** Dental **3** Salary **4** Races **5** Opulent **6** Steeple **11** Repeals **12** Aquatic **13** Russia **14** Saline **15** Latest **17** Since

101

Across **1** Bayonet **7** Adores **8** Gradual **9** Cure **10** Data **12** Goodbye **14** Destroy **16** Soil **18** Ewer **20** Measles **21** Brogue **22** Typists
Down **1** Baghdad **2** Yeast **3** Noun **4** Tallboy **5** Concedes **6** Betray **11** Alter ego **12** Gourmet **13** Enlists **15** Edward **17** Ogles **19** Lamp

102

Across **1** Absolutely **6** Strong **7** Roost **9** Tennis **10** One **11** Leer **14** Felt **15** The **16** Trader **17** Noise **18** Elopes **20** Restaurant
Down **1** Apt **2** Smoker **3** Legend **4** Thrash **5** Look over **6** Skeleton **8** Theatres **9** Televise **12** Street **13** Gateau **14** Fedora **19** Eft

103

Across **1** Elsewhere **6** Car **8** Skewer **9** Scrap **10** Gloria **11** Rashers **13** Endures **16** Corpse **18** Acted **19** Nomads **21** Eli **22** Legislate
Down **1** Elk **2** Sewer **3** Warfare **4** Erases **5** Ecarte **7** Repossess **8** Segregate **12** Ascends **14** Detail **15** Red rag **17** Rumba **20** Due

104

Across **1** Backlog **5** Copy **7** Sin **8** Torments **9** Naive **10** Sash **13** Ease **14** Scar **18** Lost **19** Times **21** Smoulder **22** Ebb **23** Stet **24** Oversee
Down **1** Business **2** Cannibal **3** Letter **4** Garish **5** Cheese **6** Pity **11** Harmless **12** Sensible **15** Robust **16** Studio **17** Starve **20** Emit

105

Across **1** Bantam **4** Fetid **7** Topsy-turvy **8** Wait **9** Latin **11** Deadpan **13** Larders **15** Sweet **17** Tees **18** Underlines **20** Trend **21** Seldom
Down **1** Brewed **2** Trot **3** Musical **4** Fatal **5** Tor **6** Doyen **7** Tirade **10** Themes **12** Nappies **14** System **15** Shunt **16** Tired **17** Tell **19** Doe

106

Across **1** Brotherhood **7** Fret **8** Enemies **9** Aid **10** Still **11** Ruined **13** Shandy **16** Veers **18** Ire **19** Ovation **20** Neat **21** Interrogate
Down **1** Bureau **2** Obtain **3** Heeded **4** Reeks **5** Opinion **6** Display **11** Ravioli **12** Inexact **13** Shinto **14** Agenda **15** Damage **17** Skier

107

Across **1** Halibut **7** Odious **8** Intends **9** Noel **10** Oast **12** Present **14** Spangle **16** Soda **18** Ulna **20** Avarice **21** Tablet **22** Expense
Down **1** Heinous **2** Lotus **3** Bang **4** To spare **5** Pianists **6** Tune in **11** Tentacle **12** Placate **13** Trapeze **15** Pillar **17** Onion **19** Gasp

108

Across **1** Wildebeest **6** String **7** Guess **9** Fennel **10** Hob **11** Afar **14** Brat **15** Tie **16** Roared **17** Reels **18** Decade **20** Blancmange
Down **1** Wet **2** Loiter **3** Engine **4** Engulf **5** Shepherd **6** Squatter **8** Sabotage **9** Farewell **12** Prison **13** Random **14** Beacon **19** Dee

109

Across **1** Mother wit **6** Rap **8** Teeter **9** Probe **10** Amulet **11** Ignites **13** Embraces **16** Notion **18** Sauna **19** Reacts **21** Sic **22** Escalator
Down **1** Mae **2** Total **3** Erratic **4** Weapon **5** Try out **7** Pheasants **8** Traverses **12** General **14** Bounce **15** Arabic **17** Trait **20** Tar

110

Across **1** Nominal **5** Fold **7** Cod **8** Prudence **9** Loose **10** Chef **13** Rope **14** Card **18** Erse **19** Tithe **21** Consider **22** Air **23** Slay **24** Resolve
Down **1** Necklace **2** Mediocre **3** Nephew **4** Launch **5** Feeler **6** Luck **11** Football **12** Rehearse **15** Dressy **16** Leader **17** Starts **20** Wool

111

Across **1** Shower **4** Avoid **7** Didgeridoo **8** Rout **9** Deeds **11** Breadth **13** Saunter **15** Tests **17** Pass **18** Behind bars **20** Rinse **21** Gadget
Down **1** Scarab **2** Writ **3** Regrets **4** Acrid **5** Odd **6** Dross **7** Duress **10** Extras **12** Handbag **14** Resent **15** Tiber **16** Singe **17** Prod **19** Hen

112

Across **1** Cheek by jowl **7** Pair **8** Tractor **9** Eat **10** Noose **11** Karate **13** Insert **16** Elver **18** Oaf **19** Cartoon **20** Acid **21** Pleased with
Down **1** Cha-cha **2** Eureka **3** Kettle **4** Yearn **5** Outcome **6** Largest **11** Kneecap **12** Reverse **13** Ironed **14** Safari **15** Radish **17** Rooks

113

Across **1** Applaud **7** Acumen **8** Abdomen **9** Tots **10** Seed **12** Prepare **14** Details **16** Edge **18** Opal **20** Termite **21** Creche **22** Retreat
Down **1** Amassed **2** Padre **3** Army **4** Dangers **5** Multiple **6** Pester **11** Deadlock **12** Plaster **13** Element **15** Expert **17** Drive **19** Grit

114

Across **1** Disability **6** Stinks **7** Teach **9** Demote **10** Sum **11** Clot **14** Real **15** Elm **16** Dollar **17** Sauce **18** Stalls **20** Persistent
Down **1** Dot **2** Sunset **3** Bishop **4** Latter **5** Transfer **6** Satchels **8** Homeless **9** Dormouse **12** Idlers **13** Closes **14** Ravage **19** Let

115

Across **1** Music hall **6** Ike **8** Sprint **9** Hated **10** Amoeba **11** Surgeon **13** Harvest **16** Edible **18** Table **19** Sitars **21** Ice **22** Smell a rat
Down **1** Map **2** Shire **3** Cutlass **4** Anchor **5** Little **7** Endangers **8** Spaghetti **12** Utensil **14** Rubies **15** Emerge **17** Inter **20** Rut

116

Across **1** Alabama **5** Saga **7** Spa **8** Tomorrow **9** Let in **10** Salt **13** Lido **14** Toil **18** Rail **19** Ideal **21** Cocktail **22** Eye **23** Stay **24** Honesty
Down **1** Absolute **2** Abattoir **3** Acting **4** Almost **5** Stroll **6** Glow **11** Timeless **12** Colliery **15** Lackey **16** Bleach **17** Violin **20** Bolt

117

Across **1** Droops **4** Cress **7** Incinerate **8** Wigs **9** Medal **11** Scalpel **13** Rarebit **15** Chair **17** Frog **18** Monotonous **20** Lager **21** Cosmos
Down **1** Drawls **2** Owns **3** Skipper **4** Cream **5** Era **6** Spell **7** Iguana **10** Debars **12** Laconic **14** Tights **15** Camel **16** Rotor **17** Fuss **19** Nag

118

Across **1** Ferris wheel **7** Club **8** Portion **9** Ova **10** Slime **11** Crater **13** Planet **16** Exits **18** Sir **19** Isolate **20** Opts **21** Heavy-handed
Down **1** Falter **2** Rub out **3** Impair **4** Warns **5** Edition **6** Lenient **11** Cherish **12** Arizona **13** Peseta **14** Abroad **15** Elated **17** Scary

119

Across **1** Surname **7** Junior **8** Residue **9** User **10** Oink **12** Hexagon **14** Stunned **16** Eros **18** Lava **20** Eternal **21** Smooth **22** Openers
Down **1** Serious **2** Resin **3** Aide **4** Ejected **5** Undulate **6** Bolero **11** Kangaroo **12** Heave-ho **13** Nestles **15** Trauma **17** Range **19** Here

120

Across **1** Gorgonzola **6** Humane **7** Never **9** Devout **10** Net **11** Goad **14** Deaf **15** Hod **16** Author **17** Gruel **18** Adapts **20** Effrontery
Down **1** Gnu **2** Roamed **3** Oregon **4** Zenith **5** Lavender **6** Hedgehog **8** Ratifies **9** Dandruff **12** Sailor **13** Attain **14** Donate **19** Try

121

Across **1** Lucrative **6** Die **8** Nimbus **9** Actor **10** Weasel **11** Veteran **13** Painter **16** Aikido **18** Peter **19** Evicts **21** Roc **22** Transient
Down **1** Lei **2** Cubes **3** Absolve **4** Infant **5** Editor **7** Erroneous **8** Newspaper **12** Erasers **14** Intact **15** Tirana **17** Knife **20** Tut

122

Across **1** Illicit **5** Milk **7** Lit **8** Reindeer **9** Shove **10** Thud **13** Mean **14** Rasp **18** Eric **19** Piece **21** Pinnacle **22** Bow **23** Gene **24** Elderly
Down **1** Illusory **2** Let loose **3** Carpet **4** Twists **5** Medium **6** Leer **11** December **12** Under way **15** Prince **16** Icicle **17** Append **20** Wise

123

Across **1** Cinder **4** Plans **7** Present-day **8** Taut **9** Horse **11** Matinee **13** Snaffle **15** Torch **17** Brie **18** Moratorium **20** Ditch **21** Echoes
Down **1** Custom **2** Dirt **3** Resumes **4** Punch **5** And **6** Style **7** Putter **10** Reform **12** Endorse **14** Events **15** Timid **16** Hatch **17** Bush **19** Rat

124

Across **1** Water pistol **7** Film **8** Dolphin **9** Toe **10** Merit **11** Tramps **13** Senses **16** Rings **18** Eft **19** Essence **20** I-spy **21** Skyscrapers
Down **1** Waiter **2** Tom-tom **3** Riders **4** Islam **5** T-shirts **6** Linctus **11** Targets **12** Amnesty **13** Sheena **14** Native **15** Erupts **17** Sonic

125

Across **1** Baboons **7** Corset **8** Rancour **9** Oust **10** Idol **12** Against **14** Glimpse **16** Taco **18** Lair **20** Draught **21** Rescue **22** Regular
Down **1** Barring **2** Bingo **3** Oboe **4** Scrooge **5** Arsonist **6** Census **11** Limerick **12** Asunder **13** Trotter **15** Leaven **17** Angel **19** Hang

126

Across **1** Natterjack **6** Opened **7** Noise **9** Pedalo **10** Ire **11** Rear **14** Talc **15** Ace **16** Animal **17** Treat **18** Entice **20** Stupendous
Down **1** Nap **2** Tanner **3** Endear **4** Jenson **5** Criminal **6** Overcast **8** Exercise **9** Pavement **12** Laptop **13** Pigeon **14** Tattoo **19** Cos

127

Across **1** Big dipper **6** Ebb **8** Gaelic **9** Tiara **10** Amuses **11** Obscene **13** Algebra **16** Riddle **18** Trier **19** Adopts **21** Ewe **22** All ends up
Down **1** Baa **2** Gulps **3** Incisor **4** Plates **5** Rebate **7** Blameless **8** Guarantee **12** Bargain **14** Guinea **15** Burial **17** Drops **20** Top

128

Across **1** Hectors **5** Norm **7** Ado **8** Politics **9** Ensue **10** Taut **13** To go **14** Lies **18** Year **19** Reeks **21** Heptagon **22** Air **23** Spry **24** Theatre
Down **1** Heavenly **2** Chop suey **3** Osprey **4** Salute **5** Not out **6** Race **11** Tolerant **12** Conserve **15** Sentry **16** Bright **17** France **20** Heap

129

Across **1** Bonsai **4** Value **7** False teeth **8** Tory **9** Loser **11** Recruit **13** Dangles **15** Basis **17** Help **18** Gargantuan **20** Scoop **21** Polite
Down **1** Boater **2** Sway **3** Insipid **4** Vital **5** Lee **6** Ether **7** Fracas **10** Spleen **12** Tank top **14** Supple **15** Bogus **16** Scamp **17** Hall **19** Rio

130

Across **1** Make believe **7** Grid **8** Reneges **9** Nib **10** Skier **11** Proper **13** Fights **16** Solve **18** Aim **19** Ignores **20** Iron **21** Good-looking
Down **1** Murder **2** Kidnap **3** Barber **4** Lands **5** English **6** Ensures **11** Passing **12** Orlando **13** Fiasco **14** Gemini **15** Throng **17** Enrol

131

Across **1** Launder **7** Abacus **8** Ceiling **9** Late **10** Jeer **12** Smother **14** Whistle **16** Atop **18** Oral **20** Panache **21** Mousse **22** Rotates
Down **1** Lockjaw **2** Unite **3** Dais **4** Ragtime **5** Valletta **6** Lustre **11** Restless **12** Slipper **13** Repress **15** Horror **17** Tacit **19** Gnat

132

Across **1** Illustrate **6** Sketch **7** Theft **9** Hearse **10** Owe **11** Agar **14** Rags **15** God **16** Enamel **17** Trout **18** Toupee **20** Celebrated
Down **1** Irk **2** Lather **3** Sphere **4** Rather **5** Teetotal **6** Straight **8** Treasure **9** Handsome **12** Gentle **13** Canter **14** Result **19** End

133

Across **1** Graveyard **6** Yes **8** Stains **9** Erase **10** Fleece **11** Raymond **13** Options **16** Savant **18** About **19** Uproar **21** Egg **22** Heartless
Down **1** Get **2** Abide **3** Eastern **4** Artery **5** Dynamo **7** Speedster **8** Suffocate **12** Assault **14** Though **15** Ottawa **17** Verge **20** Ass

134

Across **1** Capable **5** Duke **7** Van **8** Transmit **9** Noose **10** Noon **13** Tile **14** Ruin **18** Note **19** Aorta **21** Champion **22** Gut **23** Anon **24** Nominee
Down **1** Coventry **2** Pangolin **3** Bother **4** Elaine **5** Despot **6** Knit **11** Nitrogen **12** Repartee **15** Norman **16** Region **17** Magnum **20** Thin

135

Across **1** Fabric **4** Purse **7** Inimitable **8** Nuns **9** Laces **11** Sporran **13** Long leg **15** Chess **17** Rust **18** Instructor **20** Badge **21** Silver
Down **1** Faints **2** Runs **3** Comical **4** Petal **5** Rub **6** Evens **7** Income **10** Colour **12** Novices **14** Gather **15** Climb **16** Surge **17** Roll **19** Sad

136

Across **1** Inexpensive **7** Spar **8** Russell **9** Wet **10** Later **11** Dagger **13** Aflame **16** Alarm **18** Sic **19** Restore **20** Kiss **21** Mississippi
Down **1** Impala **2** Earwig **3** Porter **4** Nasal **5** Inertia **6** Enlarge **11** Diagram **12** Glasses **13** Assess **14** Lock up **15** Muesli **17** Maori

137

Across **1** Highest **7** E-mails **8** Sustain **9** Aura **10** Or so **12** Rotunda **14** Kitchen **16** Tact **18** Thus **20** Uranium **21** Allows **22** Earnest
Down **1** Hassock **2** Gusts **3** Exam **4** Tension **5** Catapult **6** Glared **11** Occasion **12** Recluse **13** Attempt **15** Inhale **17** Alive **19** Pair

138

Across **1** Determines **6** Stupor **7** Vague **9** Toilet **10** Nee **11** Pure **14** Nest **15** Inn **16** Antler **17** Eland **18** Normal **20** Meddlesome
Down **1** Dot **2** Tiptoe **3** Rarely **4** Invite **5** Engineer **6** Sapphire **8** Eventual **9** Truncate **12** Candid **13** Stance **14** Near to **19** Ace

139

Across **1** Charlatan **6** Ash **8** Decent **9** Onset **10** Tinsel **11** Iterate **13** Red tape **16** Rancid **18** Extra **19** Ascend **21** Tee **22** Raconteur
Down **1** Cue **2** Avers **3** Let slip **4** Throne **5** Nausea **7** Hot-headed **8** Detergent **12** Terrain **14** Dither **15** Arabic **17** Nacre **20** Nor

140

Across **1** Chopper **5** Copy **7** Use **8** Lacrosse **9** Lilac **10** Rues **13** Rome **14** Shot **18** Kite **19** Ambit **21** Massacre **22** Eli **23** Shoe **24** Prolong
Down **1** Churlish **2** Overlook **3** Palace **4** Recurs **5** Cooper **6** Push **11** Sombrero **12** Nestling **15** Tissue **16** Teacup **17** Gazebo **20** Cash

141

Across **1** Athens **4** Mules **7** Formidable **8** Eras **9** Licit **11** Scholar **13** Respond **15** Acres **17** Yeti **18** Bath Oliver **20** Maybe **21** Salver
Down **1** Alters **2** Eros **3** Seminar **4** Model **5** Lob **6** Scent **7** Father **10** Cooker **12** Repairs **14** Driver **15** Album **16** Scope **17** Yell **19** Toy

142

Across **1** Helping hand **7** Scut **8** Amounts **9** Tag **10** Poser **11** Scares **13** Sweats **16** Excel **18** Vet **19** Trample **20** Inch **21** Remorseless
Down **1** Hectic **2** Litter **3** Images **4** Group **5** Amnesia **6** Deserts **11** Shelter **12** Acclaim **13** Severe **14** Entire **15** Tracts **17** Leper

143

Across **1** Amalgam **7** Icarus **8** Kestrel **9** Bold **10** Ayes **12** Concept **14** Decagon **16** Eden **18** Food **20** Educate **21** Versus **22** Traders
Down **1** Awkward **2** Aisle **3** Girl **4** Million **5** Barbecue **6** Full up **11** Slapdash **12** Contest **13** Tunnels **15** Erodes **17** Drape **19** Puma

144

Across **1** Friendship **6** Credit **7** Rafts **9** Recent **10** Moo **11** Need **14** Must **15** Foe **16** Issues **17** Yeast **18** Amidst **20** Petrol bomb
Down **1** For **2** Indeed **3** Nutmeg **4** Sprite **5** Infamous **6** Crane fly **8** Short cut **9** Renegade **12** Winter **13** Assail **14** Mexico **19** Sob

145

Across **1** Equipment **6** Hum **8** Turban **9** Union **10** Scenic **11** Echelon **13** Mineral **16** Absorb **18** Tames **19** Scurry **21** Hue **22** Reluctant

Down **1** Emu **2** Urban **3** Panacea **4** Enough **5** Thrill **7** Man and boy **8** Test match **12** Classic **14** Number **15** Rascal **17** Sauna **20** Rat

146

Across **1** Replica **5** Safe **7** Son **8** Vendetta **9** Means **10** Yard **13** Sore **14** Roof **18** Nile **19** Heeds **21** Progress **22** Tor **23** Neat **24** Selects

Down **1** Rosemary **2** Pentagon **3** Invest **4** Annoys **5** Steers **6** Fate **11** Domestic **12** Censures **15** Fidget **16** Jewels **17** Chisel **20** Free

147

Across **1** Remind **4** Miser **7** God-fearing **8** Opal **9** Salad **11** Tedious **13** Dwindle **15** Terms **17** Peep **18** Eucalyptus **20** Delay **21** Direct

Down **1** Revolt **2** Idol **3** Defraud **4** Moans **5** Ski **6** Rigid **7** Gander **10** Ladies **12** Swamped **14** Export **15** Tread **16** Salty **17** Purr **19** Col

148

Across **1** Sagittarius **7** Meat **8** Attract **9** Eat **10** Chips **11** As much **13** Surety **16** Mimic **18** Arc **19** Rancour **20** Kill **21** Lion-hearted

Down **1** Shears **2** Gateau **3** Thatch **4** Attic **5** Imagine **6** Satisfy **11** Admiral **12** Memento **13** Sparta **14** Rocket **15** Toiled **17** Cloth

149

Across **1** Cabinet **7** Relief **8** Agitate **9** Tutu **10** Lash **12** Plunges **14** Smuggle **16** Menu **18** Grow **20** Average **21** Mirror **22** Dessert

Down **1** Charles **2** Bliss **3** Near **4** Tremble **5** Platinum **6** Centre **11** High wire **12** Placard **13** Student **15** Marlin **17** Evade **19** Mess

150

Across **1** Deliberate **6** Settee **7** Times **9** Patter **10** Oar **11** Bill **14** Maze **15** Ava **16** Annual **17** Drunk **18** Intact **20** Reinforces

Down **1** Due **2** Lethal **3** Bleats **4** Return **5** Temporal **6** Scabbard **8** Sergeant **9** Pleasure **12** Napkin **13** Indigo **14** Mastic **19** Cos

151

Across **1** Espionage **6** Nod **8** Motive **9** Seems **10** Repeal **11** Assists **13** Excerpt **16** Apiece **18** Aunts **19** Idiots **21** Yen **22** Exchanged
Down **1** Ego **2** Pride **3** Overlap **4** Abuses **5** Enters **7** Disasters **8** Mercenary **12** Stamina **14** Canine **15** Rustic **17** Icing **20** Ted

152

Across **1** Orchard **5** Rasp **7** Lei **8** Coleslaw **9** Occur **10** Tomb **13** Ergo **14** Eton **18** Poor **19** Races **21** Delicate **22** Ode **23** Stun **24** Enemies
Down **1** Onlooker **2** Clip-clop **3** Accord **4** Delete **5** Resume **6** Slam **11** Broccoli **12** Bolsters **15** Notion **16** Create **17** Breeze **20** Next

153

Across **1** Coyote **4** Bogus **7** Euthanasia **8** Dads **9** Strut **11** Elastic **13** Talk big **15** Medal **17** Reno **18** Meticulous **20** Smell **21** Yields
Down **1** Candle **2** Onus **3** Exhibit **4** Banns **5** Gas **6** Smart **7** Edward **10** Rubies **12** Cavalry **14** Globes **15** Mumps **16** Local **17** Ruse **19** Tie

154

Across **1** Fashionable **7** Oral **8** Immense **9** Ado **10** Shave **11** Brainy **13** Expect **16** After **18** Ill **19** Handbag **20** Iota **21** Grandfather
Down **1** Former **2** Salami **3** Idiocy **4** Names **5** Bandage **6** Element **11** Bear hug **12** Antenna **13** Enigma **14** Polish **15** Canter **17** Rabid

155

Across **1** Demigod **7** Exhale **8** Prisons **9** Lard **10** Seer **12** Gorilla **14** Tuesday **16** Halt **18** Find **20** Isolate **21** Tennis **22** Happens
Down **1** Deposit **2** Maine **3** Good **4** Destroy **5** Childish **6** Floral **11** Resident **12** Garnish **13** Actress **15** United **17** Amaze **19** Soup

156

Across **1** Capitalism **6** Propel **7** Dance **9** Seance **10** Tug **11** Peat **14** Both **15** Leo **16** Slogan **17** Theme **18** Nature **20** Crispbread
Down **1** Car **2** Puppet **3** Talons **4** Ladder **5** Sanction **6** Pamphlet **8** Egg white **9** Saboteur **12** Assets **13** Hobnob **14** Battle **19** Rod

157

Across **1** Objective **6** Cod **8** Glider **9** Items **10** Trusty **11** Operate **13** Combine **16** Retina **18** Arson **19** Expand **21** Hoe **22** Sceptical

Down **1** Oil **2** Judas **3** Carry on **4** Inside **5** Eczema **7** Disregard **8** Gate-crash **12** Perfect **14** Misses **15** Innate **17** Topic **20** Nil

158

Across **1** Magenta **5** Sari **7** Lea **8** Grimaces **9** Cadet **10** Room **13** Wide **14** Loot **18** None **19** Terse **21** All clear **22** Ice **23** Anon **24** Dusters

Down **1** Molecule **2** Grandson **3** Negate **4** Apiary **5** Shadow **6** Reel **11** Migraine **12** Referees **15** Toucan **16** Defend **17** Starts **20** Clan

159

Across **1** Abates **4** Tight **7** Misfortune **8** Edam **9** Yacht **11** Swindon **13** Natural **15** Trend **17** Soot **18** Proficient **20** Dunce **21** Submit

Down **1** Adders **2** Trim **3** Saffron **4** Tarry **5** Gnu **6** Treat **7** Marine **10** Carrot **12** Nappies **14** Latest **15** Tepid **16** Drive **17** Snub **19** Own

160

Across **1** Expenditure **7** Fell **8** Glaring **9** Fig **10** Spool **11** Regret **13** Pranks **16** Panic **18** Roe **19** Shrieks **20** Numb **21** Enlargement

Down **1** Emerge **2** Pilfer **3** Nugget **4** Imams **5** Unicorn **6** Engulfs **11** Riposte **12** General **13** Pursue **14** Avenue **15** Kismet **17** Clear

161

Across **1** Harbour **7** Eclair **8** Ailment **9** Duck **10** Herd **12** Cure-all **14** Notable **16** Noon **18** Nazi **20** Elusive **21** Bought **22** Offends

Down **1** Heathen **2** Ruler **3** Open **4** Retinue **5** Bludgeon **6** Fiscal **11** Dealings **12** Close to **13** Lingers **15** Orator **17** Onion **19** Gulf

162

Across **1** Nosy parker **6** Sniper **7** Crust **9** Second **10** Arm **11** Door **14** Pear **15** Old **16** Pallid **17** Swede **18** Narrow **20** Assessment

Down **1** Nun **2** Supper **3** Pardon **4** Recede **5** Emulated **6** Studious **8** Tomorrow **9** Soldiers **12** Sphere **13** Blinds **14** Pierce **19** Opt

163

Across **1** Godfather **6** Air **8** Stylus **9** Roses **10** Meteor **11** Eternal **13** Confuse **16** Triple **18** Louts **19** Nudist **21** Nee **22** Assistant
Down **1** Get **2** Delve **3** Assures **4** Hearse **5** Raisin **7** Resilient **8** Semicolon **12** Tetanus **14** Nausea **15** Upsets **17** India **20** Sot

164

Across **1** Octagon **5** Card **7** Tar **8** Verbatim **9** Odour **10** Adam **13** To-do **14** Also **18** Erse **19** Theft **21** Alienate **22** Ann **23** Sell **24** Endless
Down **1** Optional **2** Tortoise **3** Govern **4** Normal **5** Cravat **6** Rain **11** Moderate **12** Contents **15** Ordeal **16** Decade **17** Attend **20** Flee

165

Across **1** Remark **4** Lifts **7** Baton round **8** Ever **9** Sings **11** Tractor **13** Wanders **15** Sweet **17** Pest **18** Los Angeles **20** Night **21** Salmon
Down **1** Resent **2** Ajar **3** Know-how **4** Lords **5** Flu **6** Sides **7** Berate **10** Nieces **12** Rashers **14** Saturn **15** Salon **16** Tenet **17** Peal **19** Sag

166

Across **1** Bullfighter **7** Comb **8** Useless **9** Egg **10** Tutor **11** Vessel **13** Cheese **16** Tiles **18** Our **19** Reasons **20** Iron **21** Neanderthal
Down **1** Bronze **2** Labels **3** Frugal **4** Great **5** Theatre **6** Reserve **11** Veteran **12** Sultana **13** Closer **14** Enrich **15** Stroll **17** Sword

167

Across **1** Glamour **7** Ensues **8** Loafers **9** Else **10** Acne **12** Bullish **14** Thistle **16** Sofa **18** Data **20** Drivers **21** Decide **22** Robbery
Down **1** Gallant **2** Again **3** Oxen **4** Residue **5** As well as **6** Census **11** Ecstatic **12** Blender **13** Hearsay **15** Heaven **17** Obese **19** Limb

168

Across **1** Collarbone **6** Mental **7** Nomad **9** Reggae **10** Tic **11** Tour **14** Bear **15** Ali **16** Larder **17** Erase **18** Devise **20** Kettledrum
Down **1** Cue **2** Letter **3** Allege **4** Bunker **5** No matter **6** Mortgage **8** Decorate **9** Ruminate **12** Albeit **13** Bridge **14** Beaver **19** Sum

169

Across **1** Postnatal **6** Out **8** Beside **9** Cramp **10** Weasel **11** Eastern **13** Tempest **16** Tartar **18** Haste **19** Cancan **21** Sir **22** Sandshoes
Down **1** Pie **2** Spins **3** Needles **4** Traces **5** Locate **7** Tip and run **8** Bewitches **12** Attacks **14** Misers **15** Eleven **17** Ringo **20** Ass

170

Across **1** Arsenic **5** Jest **7** Rap **8** Darkroom **9** Valet **10** Stop **13** Note **14** Rank **18** Tale **19** Octet **21** Marathon **22** Gun **23** Stye **24** Resolve
Down **1** Aardvark **2** Supplant **3** Nudity **4** Caress **5** Jargon **6** Soon **11** Portugal **12** Sentence **15** Karate **16** Tether **17** Counts **20** Salt

171

Across **1** Scampi **4** Awful **7** Profitable **8** Week **9** Rides **11** Primate **13** Entitle **15** Ether **17** Tuba **18** Body warmer **20** Rugby **21** Shrill
Down **1** Show up **2** Mark **3** Inflate **4** Actor **5** Fib **6** Leeds **7** Perish **10** Detour **12** Ensures **14** Enamel **15** Ember **16** Rowdy **17** Tear **19** Dig

172

Across **1** Olive branch **7** Span **8** Praises **9** Owe **10** Solve **11** Detest **13** Dressy **16** Super **18** Rod **19** Include **20** Earl **21** Golden syrup
Down **1** Oppose **2** Ignore **3** Expert **4** Roars **5** Nestles **6** Hosiery **11** Dashing **12** Topical **13** Duress **14** Endear **15** Stir up **17** Route

173

Across **1** Picador **7** Utopia **8** Ruction **9** Pate **10** Soil **12** Present **14** Lay open **16** Rear **18** Emma **20** Asinine **21** Dumdum **22** Earnest
Down **1** Parasol **2** Cacti **3** Drip **4** Runcorn **5** Composer **6** Listen **11** Leopards **12** Pen name **13** Torment **15** Armour **17** Elite **19** Pier

174

Across **1** Photograph **6** Spades **7** Thumb **9** Arrest **10** Ewe **11** Cops **14** Scar **15** One **16** Coffee **17** Slime **18** Infant **20** Benefactor
Down **1** Pop **2** Orders **3** Oyster **4** Rotate **5** Prudence **6** Spacious **8** Beetroot **9** Appetite **12** Scheme **13** Africa **14** See fit **19** Nor

175

Across **1** Nocturnal **6** Awn **8** Spread **9** Inter **10** Prance **11** Steeple **13** Refresh **16** Imbibe **18** Twice **19** Bosses **21** Rue **22** Desperate
Down **1** Nip **2** Clean **3** Undress **4** Novice **5** Laptop **7** Nerveless **8** Superstar **12** Thimble **14** Foiled **15** Events **17** Basra **20** Eye

176

Across **1** Pelican **5** Cold **7** Inn **8** Retrieve **9** Needs **10** Vain **13** Cone **14** Nail **18** East **19** There **21** Customer **22** Ire **23** Fear **24** Shortly
Down **1** Poignant **2** Lingerie **3** Cerise **4** Native **5** Clinic **6** Love **11** Novelist **12** Cemetery **15** Latter **16** Stamps **17** Stereo **20** Huge

177

Across **1** Sapper **4** Throb **7** Sunday best **8** Tram **9** Earth **11** Copycat **13** Laments **15** Sheen **17** Ague **18** Turn turtle **20** Ranch **21** Annoys
Down **1** Static **2** Plum **3** Radical **4** Thyme **5** Roe **6** Bitch **7** Sample **10** Renege **12** Taverna **14** Sweats **15** Sitar **16** Notch **17** Alan **19** Run

178

Across **1** Red squirrel **7** Tutu **8** Abstain **9** Bar **10** Tithe **11** Celery **13** Exodus **16** Mocks **18** Lit **19** Amnesia **20** Puny **21** Decelerates
Down **1** Rouble **2** Double **3** Quarry **4** Inset **5** Reacted **6** Lancets **11** Command **12** Laconic **13** Eclair **14** Output **15** Uranus **17** Sisal

179

Across **1** Mascara **7** Barley **8** Mustard **9** Urdu **10** Oink **12** Sticker **14** Hideous **16** Shop **18** Loss **20** Engrave **21** Tackle **22** Derides
Down **1** Mammoth **2** Susan **3** Afar **4** Abducts **5** Trounces **6** Meddle **11** Keepsake **12** Succeed **13** Repress **15** Isobar **17** Hoard **19** Agar

180

Across **1** Chatterbox **6** Bottle **7** Bacon **9** To boot **10** Sap **11** Horn **14** Bolt **15** Own **16** Ration **17** Miami **18** Embalm **20** Determined
Down **1** Coo **2** Action **3** Tremor **4** Robots **5** Occasion **6** Bathroom **8** Nepotism **9** Truncate **12** Bruise **13** Stream **14** Bobbin **19** Lad

181

Across **1** Harmonica **6** Tor **8** Stigma **9** Equip **10** Bistro **11** Lodgers **13** Repeals **16** Pirate **18** Canoe **19** Erupts **21** Sue **22** Transient
Down **1** Hat **2** Right **3** On a roll **4** Indeed **5** Attune **7** Repossess **8** Subtracts **12** Ospreys **14** Punnet **15** Agenda **17** Rouge **20** Tot

182

Across **1** Bid fair **5** Vast **7** Aim **8** Divulged **9** Forge **10** Goat **13** Rote **14** Rare **18** Acre **19** Noose **21** Charming **22** Got **23** Here **24** Learner
Down **1** Bradford **2** Demerara **3** Audrey **4** Ravage **5** Vulgar **6** Seed **11** Toboggan **12** Deserter **15** Ecarte **16** Menial **17** Enigma **20** Shoe

183

Across **1** Pistol **4** Cease **7** Kingfisher **8** Noel **9** Bible **11** Central **13** Lexicon **15** Delta **17** Next **18** Tie-breaker **20** Mitre **21** Detain
Down **1** Picnic **2** Tail **3** Logical **4** Climb **5** Ash **6** Eerie **7** Kennel **10** Bicker **12** Leotard **14** Notion **15** Datum **16** Agree **17** Neat **19** Eat

184

Across **1** Quicksilver **7** Kiwi **8** Epsilon **9** Cop **10** E-mail **11** Ernest **13** Slates **16** Topic **18** Ebb **19** Abusive **20** Echo **21** Trendsetter
Down **1** Quiver **2** Icicle **3** Keep at **4** Issue **5** Valiant **6** Rankles **11** Extract **12** Neptune **13** Sleeve **14** Albert **15** Either **17** Child

185

Across **1** Cabbage **7** Leader **8** Plumage **9** Kerb **10** Opts **12** Snapper **14** Suspect **16** Reef **18** Liar **20** Termite **21** Gentle **22** Regrets
Down **1** Copious **2** Blunt **3** Arab **4** Elegant **5** Larkspur **6** George **11** Separate **12** Scooter **13** Rafters **15** United **17** Exile **19** Brag

186

Across **1** Candyfloss **6** Abseil **7** Weird **9** Decode **10** Boa **11** Iris **14** Snow **15** Ant **16** Excite **17** Later **18** Expend **20** Iron maiden
Down **1** Cub **2** Nieces **3** Yellow **4** Lawyer **5** Shinbone **6** All in all **8** Deadwood **9** Dictator **12** Tehran **13** Eczema **14** Stupid **19** Nun

187

Across **1** Accordion **6** Old **8** Pencil **9** Asset **10** Impala **11** Stetson **13** Empower **16** Assist **18** Easel **19** Hounds **21** See **22** Dastardly
Down **1** Ape **2** Cocoa **3** Release **4** Inhale **5** Noises **7** Detonates **8** Priceless **12** Trachea **14** Pushed **15** Walrus **17** Squad **20** Day

188

Across **1** Penguin **5** Rock **7** Egg **8** Jodhpurs **9** Hates **10** Evil **13** Role **14** Real **18** Poor **19** Andre **21** One-sided **22** Era **23** Keen **24** En masse
Down **1** Plethora **2** Nightcap **3** Unjust **4** Nudges **5** Repair **6** Cork **11** Loudness **12** Relegate **15** Loosen **16** Cradle **17** Tandem **20** Once

189

Across **1** Rustic **4** Tenor **7** Tournament **8** Abut **9** Ashes **11** Kneecap **13** Singers **15** Month **17** Deer **18** Unemployed **20** Ebony **21** Obtain
Down **1** Remark **2** Trot **3** Caracas **4** Tiara **5** Nee **6** Rates **7** Tune in **10** Heeded **12** Piccolo **14** Screen **15** Mouse **16** Happy **17** Deft **19** Ego

190

Across **1** Paracetamol **7** Eros **8** Trawler **9** Sit **10** Lithe **11** Rebate **13** Cigars **16** Clubs **18** Ice **19** Locusts **20** Lout **21** Strait-laced
Down **1** Purple **2** Russia **3** Cattle **4** Trail **5** Militia **6** Larders **11** Recalls **12** Bouncer **13** Chisel **14** Gaelic **15** Rotund **17** Sushi

191

Across **1** Mug shot **7** Abacus **8** Let down **9** Main **10** Acts **12** Arrange **14** Descend **16** Drab **18** Pill **20** Nirvana **21** Bodkin **22** Artiste
Down **1** Mallard **2** Get at **3** Hoot **4** Tankard **5** Farm hand **6** Outing **11** Suchlike **12** Antenna **13** Embrace **15** Editor **17** Reaps **19** Fret

192

Across **1** Laboratory **6** Cosset **7** Traps **9** Soiree **10** Toe **11** Atop **14** Pose **15** Dub **16** Uneven **17** Reeks **18** Craven **20** Cotton wool
Down **1** Leo **2** Bishop **3** Return **4** Totter **5** Reaction **6** Colander **8** Skeleton **9** Sombrero **12** Russet **13** Beacon **14** Pedalo **19** Eel

193

Across **1** Handcuffs **6** Art **8** Stance **9** Gouda **10** Turtle **11** Natters **13** Rosette **16** Rattle **18** Tibia **19** Strays **21** Sol **22** Excellent
Down **1** Hit **2** Nonet **3** Clement **4** Flight **5** Salute **7** Transfers **8** Saturates **12** Aerosol **14** Subtle **15** Tragic **17** Terse **20** Yet

194

Across **1** Iceberg **5** Teak **7** Foe **8** Cardigan **9** Nacre **10** Go in **13** Aura **14** Toss **18** Earn **19** Obese **21** Dandruff **22** Out **23** Gene **24** Honesty
Down **1** Infinite **2** Exercise **3** Exceed **4** Garage **5** Trivia **6** Ajar **11** Numerous **12** Patently **15** Saddle **16** Enough **17** Boffin **20** Vase

195

Across **1** Garlic **4** Radio **7** Courageous **8** Halt **9** Desks **11** Cartoon **13** Nothing **15** Enter **17** Plan **18** Hopping mad **20** Reels **21** Number
Down **1** Gothic **2** Loot **3** Carrion **4** Rigid **5** Duo **6** Oasis **7** Claret **10** Shield **12** Nonagon **14** Gander **15** Ether **16** Reins **17** Palm **19** Pie

196

Across **1** In miniature **7** Spar **8** Murders **9** Ire **10** Larva **11** Dreary **13** Mighty **16** Arena **18** Rim **19** Run riot **20** Idle **21** Millionaire
Down **1** Impair **2** Marina **3** Namely **4** April **5** Unearth **6** Ecstasy **11** Diagram **12** Eternal **13** Martin **14** Gemini **15** Twelve **17** Alibi

197

Across **1** Husband **7** Amulet **8** Albumen **9** Also **10** Fare **12** Traipse **14** Resumes **16** Nazi **18** Data **20** Average **21** Select **22** Extinct
Down **1** Head for **2** Sober **3** Army **4** Dangers **5** Eurasian **6** Versus **11** Educated **12** Testate **13** Evident **15** Erases **17** Again **19** Heat

198

Across **1** Mayonnaise **6** Starve **7** Looks **9** Bedlam **10** Eli **11** Tear **14** Slim **15** Emu **16** Outlay **17** Satan **18** Arable **20** Mercantile
Down **1** Mat **2** Yorker **3** Needle **4** Aflame **5** Slovenly **6** Spotless **8** Shipmate **9** Baguette **12** Cognac **13** Strain **14** Safari **19** Lee

199

Across **1** Fictional **6** Eye **8** Street **9** Magic **10** Reason **11** Sangria **13** Negates **16** Spring **18** Lemur **19** Unties **21** Ski **22** Tightrope
Down **1** Fat **2** Cress **3** Intense **4** Norman **5** Ledger **7** Exchanges **8** Strangles **12** Assault **14** Gambit **15** Throng **17** Ratio **20** Ewe

200

Across **1** Haddock **5** Ugly **7** Sob **8** Tungsten **9** Tense **10** Amid **13** Doze **14** Thin **18** Rose **19** Ernie **21** Assassin **22** Ago **23** Errs **24** Measles
Down **1** Hesitate **2** Debonair **3** Outset **4** Kansas **5** Unsaid **6** Lees **11** Downfall **12** Generous **15** Nomads **16** Jetsam **17** Hernia **20** User